# Enough is Enough

## How to Stop Emotional Overeating

### CAROL LOOK

## Legal Disclaimers and Notices

Copyright© 2013 Velocity House

ISBN: 978-1624090196

# Table of Contents

# INTRODUCTION

*It's going to be a long day.*

That's your first thought as you wake up in the morning. Slowly you crawl out of bed, bleary-eyed and with a slight headache from all the sugar you ate last night. You wander to the bathroom, curious after a long night's sleep whether you've lost any weight yet on your current diet. You step on the scale. You think you might have gained a pound or two. You check. It's true, you've gained a pound and a half…for the third week in a row.

Not the way you wanted to start your day… again.

On the way to work you try to decide whether your routine latte counts as "cheating" on your diet. "Well, I won't be able to function without my coffee," you think. You duck into the nearest shop and order a latte—the largest size possible. You feel a pang of guilt about the calories, but you vow to cut back at lunch.

You reach work ten minutes late. Your boss chews you out for tardiness. Your boss stops you and yells at you as you pass his office getting back to your desk. You drink down half your latte. You feel warm and comfortable.

The sensation quickly disappears when you see your workload for the day. There's no way you're going to be able to get all this done in time. It's simply too much. You get started, but you can't focus. Eventually you stand up and wander to the kitchen area. There's a vending machine. You grab a snack and bring it back to your desk, idly munching as you continue slogging through the day's tasks.

Lunch has finally arrived! Forgetting your earlier vow, and feeling stressed from how much work you've done, you decide to "reward" yourself with an oversized meal and large soda. Again, you feel guilty for cheating on your diet, but this feels urgent. You're so tired you know you'll need the energy later.

The second half of the day goes by just as slowly as the first. You still can't get any work done, or not enough. You know if you're not done by five you'll have to stay late, and at this point you're resigned to that fact. It's going to be a late night. You grab a soda and another snack from the kitchen to keep your energy level up as five comes and goes. Your boss comes by and stands over your shoulder for a while, nagging you about not having your work done. You can feel your temper rising, but you shove some food in your mouth to help you stay focused. It's hard for you to stay angry when you're eating.

On the way home you glance at the clock and realize how late it is. "I don't want to cook tonight," you say to nobody in particular. You stop instead at the nearest fast food place and order more than usual. "Oh well," you say, "I'll just save the leftovers if I have to."

You finally stumble through the door, three hours late and feeling like you've reached rock bottom. You slam the door shut, head into the living room with your fast food, flip on the TV and start eating. You feel numb.

You weigh yourself before bed. The scale says you've gained just under four pounds today. "It's probably not accurate," you think. "I just ate dinner. I'll wait and weigh myself in the morning."

At some point in the night you get up and can't fall back asleep because of your anxiety about all the deadlines you have to meet at your job. You wander to the kitchen, stare into the fridge, and finally decide to eat something. You snack for a while before you head back to bed.

The next morning, you weigh yourself again. You didn't gain four pounds yesterday, but you did gain two. You sigh and vow to "be better" today.

Sound familiar?

Emotional overeating is a huge challenge I have worked on for years with my clients. They have the desire to stick to their diet, they don't want to overeat, but they feel intense food cravings during the day and can't seem to control what or when they eat. This is all because of underlying negative emotions.

Stress. Anger. Loneliness. Anxiety. Fear. Boredom: these are common emotions people are afraid of feeling—so they use eating excess food to calm themselves down. When they encounter these feelings, they begin craving food, assume that they're hungry and start eating.

Why? Food actually helps "numb" or distract you from these negative emotions, so for a short time you feel happier. You feel comfortable. As you're eating you block out why you were stressed or angry or lonely or anxious.

Of course, this is only a temporary solution. Eventually those emotions resurface, and you're forced to either confront them or eat again. On top of that, you may have an additional feeling of shame because of your poor eating habits. It's a frustrating cycle.

It doesn't have to be that way. ***In this book I'm going to teach you how to handle your emotions, master your eating habits, and regain control of your life.***

Gone will be the days when you start snacking on a bag of chips while watching TV only to look down and notice half the bag is gone. You'll stop feeling like you need to eat a big meal to "reward" yourself for surviving through a hectic day. You'll no longer get up in the middle of the night to grab a quick bite to eat to quiet some unnamed anxiety.

This book contains knowledge I've accumulated through years of working with emotional overeaters. I know how insurmountable this problem can seem, because I used food to quiet my stress for years. But I'm willing to help because I know support and relief is available. With the right tools, you *can* regain control. It's not impossible.

You simply need to keep reading to find out how!

# CHAPTER ONE

## Emotional Overeating

I've worked to help people handle their emotions now for most of my life, and you know what? I'm still amazed by how powerful emotions are—how much they provide the fuel that runs our lives.

Emotional overeating is the behavior of using food to calm down your emotions.[1] Instead of eating for nutrition or because your body is hungry, you eat to protect yourself from uncomfortable emotions. You end up eating because of some underlying emotional stress in your life, and food is there to comfort you.

Food can sometimes become a "drug" for people, serving the same purpose as alcohol or cocaine.[2] It's tasty, it comes in many different forms, but the way it's acting upon your mind and body is the same as any other drug.

Do you ever feel like an addict when it comes to food? Do you ever swear off sugar or chips or bread only to find yourself indulging again when you're upset or stressed out?

What's your drug of choice? Is it chocolate? Sugar? Steak? Potato chips? Soda?

Maybe you swear off your drug one day. You quit cold turkey. People do that, right? I've certainly done it before. You say to yourself, "Okay, body, we're not going to eat unhealthy foods any more. We're done eating potato chips." Maybe you even succeed for a while! You go a week or two without eating chips. You feel less sluggish, you lose a few pounds, and you're happy with your self-restraint. You improve both mentally and physically.

Then you're walking through the grocery store and almost unconsciously throw a bag of chips into your cart. You rationalize it to yourself. "This time I'll be better. I don't even crave chips anymore. I'll just eat a few at a time."

You get home and unpack your groceries. When you're done you feel like you deserve a little reward for your trouble, so you open up your bag of chips. You eat one. Then another.

After a few minutes of mindless eating you look down to notice half the bag is already gone! Where did all those chips go? You hide the bag in the cupboard, ashamed at your lack of self-control.

This cycle has an addictive feel to it—you swear off the "substance" only to return to it when times are tough. You know it's bad for you, but you do it anyway. You start out with the best of intentions, but inevitably fall back into old patterns of behavior.

I often compare people who overeat to those who smoke. It's not that my patients who smoked thought it was a great idea. They knew all the risks, all the drawbacks. They simply could not seem to break the habit, no matter how hard they tried. Smoking is incredibly difficult to stop, for the same reasons overeating is hard to stop—it works to numb your emotions.

Early on I found that working with clients who were overweight was similarly difficult to working with smokers. My clients often forgot to keep up with their program between sessions, or abandoned their sessions entirely. They both start their bad habit again for the same reason – hoping to numb uncomfortable emotions.

When you "fall off the wagon," you generate even more negative emotion, deepening your feelings of shame and self-hatred. Overeating is an unhealthy coping mechanism, and one that must be addressed. However, it doesn't make sense to address it by "quitting food" cold turkey.

Quitting cold turkey is very challenging, and addicts and alcoholics are asked to get sober this way. Some people can deal with the strain it puts on them, mentally and physically, if they have enough support. When someone feels "addicted" to food, of course they can't quit cold turkey—they need to eat to survive.

Overeating represents, at its heart, a loss of control. Food starts to control your life. Overeating becomes a compulsion—a behavior you can't control. Many of my clients describe a loss of choice when it comes to when and what they eat. It's not that they want to keep eating. They just can't seem to stop. One of my clients even told me she couldn't wait to go to sleep at night, because it meant an end to her out of control eating for a few hours. She had grown to resent food consumption, but her mind wouldn't let her stop. Many times she'd find herself staring into the fridge, wondering why she was there. She didn't need more food, but it seemed like a great idea to eat. This pattern mimics what an alcoholic describes experiencing, as well.

There are numerous types of emotional overeating I've encountered. Each involves consuming more food more often than your body actually needs to function simply because of some hidden emotional issue.

See if you recognize yourself in any of these situations.

One of the most common aspects of emotional overeating is eating to avoid or numb any painful emotions.[3] This has become a bit of a stereotype in films and other media. Picture the woman who was just dumped by her boyfriend shoveling ice cream and chocolate bars into her mouth. When it's presented in the context of a film we laugh, but then we do it to ourselves.

When things go wrong, we eat to stifle our emotions. Have you ever wondered why people eat ice cream or other junk food when things go wrong? It's because eating works to temporarily make them feel better. Some of these people might only use food to calm their emotions; maybe they only eat poorly when things go really poorly. For others, it's a way of life. All emotions are scary to them, so they eat constantly to avoid feeling anything.

In fact, this destructive overeating crops up as a coping mechanism for almost every negative emotion. Anger is a common emotion I see my clients try to avoid. Maybe they get in a fight or butt heads with their boss at work. Then they head home and eat an entire bag of chips or order a large pizza and dive right in. People know it's not healthy, but they just don't care. They *need* the food in order to calm down.

Stress eating also falls under this category.[4] This form of overeating is doubly dangerous because some people already tend to put on weight when they're stressed. When our job or family life adds even more stress, it's tempting to eat lots of unhealthy food to take the edge off of our irritability. We think maybe if we eat our stress levels will go down. I've actually found the opposite to be true. Once people overeat, they start stressing about how much food they just consumed. Their stress levels go down *while* eating, but actually go up after they've finished.

Loneliness is another key emotion that leads to overeating. Food takes the place of friendship. This is especially dangerous because it's a reinforcing cycle. The more someone overeats, the more likely their self-esteem suffers. They'll stop feeling as social, so the feelings of loneliness will increase and they'll hide out in isolation more often.

Frequently, people don't   recognize negative emotions, such as anxiety or fear, and they just start eating to satisfy the nagging urge to put something in their mouth.

For instance, how often have you been sitting around during the day or late at night, between meals, and felt the urge to snack on something? You can't even tell if you're actually hungry, but your body *feels* hungry. The more you concentrate on that urge, the more you feel like you have to eat something, even if you know your body doesn't need more food.

You go to the kitchen, grab some snack food, and chow down. Once you start, you feel like you can't stop eating. You just want more and more food.

Or maybe you're sitting in front of the television when the urge to eat hits. You grab food and bring it back to the living room, snacking while you watch your show.

Before long you realize you've eaten way more than you intended. You just meant to snack, but now you've eaten practically an entire meal made up of empty calories. You put the snack away, determined not to let it happen again. The next time you're watching television, however, you end up repeating this cycle.

This sort of overeating—when you're bored or distracted—is something I see in clients time and time again. They don't mean to eat so much, but it's as if their mind sees eating as something to fill the time instead of as a necessity. Easy access to junk food makes this problem especially widespread. All they have to do is go to the kitchen, where they've most likely stocked up on unhealthy snacks already.

The truth is, the problem is not about the food!

Emotional eating is hard to combat because you feel such an urgency to quiet your feelings, and it's difficult to get to the emotional roots of this problem when you are facing it alone. With guidance, support, and introspection, together we can address the underlying issues.

Emotional overeating can even occur in people who seem perfectly happy. I refer to this as eating to sabotage your success. You've made it to a point in life where, with a little more work, you could achieve your dreams. Instead of embracing that potential, you shy away from it. You start eating too much in an effort to derail your momentum. You're afraid of success.

All of the above examples raise the question, why do we overeat? What, fundamentally, causes the overeating cycle to be so challenging?

The heart of the problem is that emotional overeating *works*. It *does* numb our emotions, for a short time. It seems crazy that overeating could have such a deep effect on our systems, but food and binge-eating absolutely manipulate how we feel.

Studies postulate it's the physical act of eating that helps us ignore our feelings. We use it to narrow our span of attention. In this theory, eating is just active enough that it causes us to concentrate on what we're doing, allowing us to shut out our subconscious. All of our emotions, our worries, become "less important" to the brain, as it focuses on getting food.

Another study, conducted by the University of Southampton, found that women who were exposed to cues simulating loneliness or anger ate significantly more in the aftermath of that event.[5] This shows there's definitely a correlation between negative emotions and overeating. The problem only grows when those negative emotions arise internally instead of from external cues.

Whatever the psychological reason, it's clear emotional overeating does "help."[6] That is to say, even knowing the long-term physical problems caused by overeating, we keep doing it because it helps anesthetize difficult feelings for a period of time. It protects us from what we don't want to feel.

Going through a divorce? Under a lot of stress at work? Feeling lonely and abandoned by former friends? Emotional overeating seems like a solution, because it can take your mind off those feelings.

Emotional overeating is a *relief.*

We don't even stop long enough to weigh the short-term relief versus the long-term effects; we just overeat without thinking. The long-term effects are incredibly serious—excessive weight gain increases risk factors for heart disease, diabetes, and cancer. We know it's not good for us.

But that relief is so pleasant. It feels wonderful to ignore those feelings for a little bit longer, until the food runs out.

When we look at the reasons behind emotional overeating, it doesn't seem so daunting. We can identify the causes: "If I'm angry, I eat," or, "If I'm lonely, I eat." Since knowing the problem is the first step towards fixing the problem, we often think we're set.[7] We've identified the issue, and now we just have to remain vigilant.

Overeating is extremely hard to fight, however.

Let's look at a serious addiction—alcoholism—a crippling affliction. It can tear apart families or cause horrendous health issues down the line. It's difficult to fight, and people often relapse multiple times. Most recovering alcoholics never get to feel they "beat" alcoholism. Instead, they feel as if they've temporarily remained sober. One drink could bring all that old bad behavior back in minutes.

Because of this, most alcoholics are told to stay away from situations involving alcohol. For instance, an alcoholic should stay away from bars. A bar exists solely to provide alcohol, so it's an easy place for an alcoholic to relapse. The more an alcoholic minimizes contact with alcohol, the better his or her chances to overcome the addiction. You can't relapse as an alcoholic if there's never any alcohol around.

Now think of that same option, in terms of overeating. What do you tell the person who uses food the way an alcoholic uses a drink? Someone who's "addicted" to food? Sure, if it's a certain *type* of food (chips, for example, or ice cream) you can avoid keeping those in the house; that should help.

But if you're just chronically using food to avoid feelings…you can't quit eating cold turkey! It doesn't work that way. For someone whose primary coping mechanism is overeating when they're stressed out, life is a constant struggle. There's always food within reach. There's no way to escape it. It's extremely unfair. You're constantly confronted with the "drug of your choice." It's like a recovering alcoholic who works in a bar, or an ex-smoker whose friends give him cigarettes for his birthday. The constant temptation is cruel.

Overeating is a multifaceted, complex issue. It affects your professional and personal life, harming relationships and causing inner turmoil.

It doesn't matter who you are. I've worked on this issue with older clients who've already attained success in life, but now can't stop putting on the pounds. I've worked with younger clients, just starting off on their careers, who know their overeating is holding them back. I've worked with men and women of all shapes and sizes. This is not a rare affliction. It's all too prevalent in our society. Some of my clients were stressed, some ate away their anger, some were avoiding loneliness. Some simply ate because they sat at a computer all day.

Most people can probably identify with one of the above situations, if only on a superficial level. Not everyone will have a debilitating addiction to overeating, but most everyone has at least used food to anesthetize feelings a few times in their life. Its prominent role in media (the girl with a pint of ice cream) has made it almost an accepted and iconic part of our culture.

Okay, we all know what emotional overeating is. Now how do we stop it? How do we put down the chips, give up the ice cream, and break the eternal cycle of consumption?

Which feelings are you eating to ignore? Which feelings are you most afraid of? Why do you eat when you aren't hungry? Why do you eat more than you need? Why do you overeat when you've promised yourself you won't?

Are you afraid of the answers to these questions? Don't be. That's a common reaction with many people. They want to stop overeating, but they're afraid to find out *why* they overeat. Hunting down the underlying issues behind unhealthy habits is an incredibly personal journey. But it's frightening to confront these issues—what if it reveals some ugly truth?

It's unhealthy to stifle your emotions. It's even unhealthier to stifle those emotions with food. Confronting your overeating might not be the most glamorous task you undertake in life, but you're going to feel like a brand new person afterward. You're going to be the one in charge of your body again, instead of the other way around. All you need is a little help and guidance to get to that point.

I know how scary it is to feel like you don't have control over your behavior. We like to think that we're always ready to take on any challenge. We want that sense of control in life. We want to control our own destiny. We want to be self-sustaining and independent.

Unfortunately, this means we also tend to ignore help when it's offered. This is the mindset for most addicts:

"I can stop any day. I don't need to be unhealthy. I'm not addicted. I *choose* to continue this behavior." Despite how prevalent this attitude is, it's a lie in all but the rarest cases. Most addicts, or people who use any kind of substance addictively, like it or not, need some help and support in order to overcome these obstacles.

I can offer that help. By the time you've read this book, you will have all the tools you need to fight your own battle against emotional overeating. I've now been using the techniques in this book to help myself and others in the struggle for over 15 years, and I can tell you it works.

Now that doesn't mean you won't have some challenges here. For this process to work, it will require effort on your part. You're going to be an active, engaged participant in addressing the emotional issues underlying your overeating. If you refuse to confront the cause of your overeating, we'll never make progress. This is a shared responsibility. I give you the tools; you put them to use.

I believe in you, though. I have faith if I provide you with the right techniques you'll be able to turn your life around. Don't be a slave to food anymore! I know how easy it is to succumb, but you have to fight back! Food's everywhere and it's incredibly tempting. It's a challenge, but I know you've got the determination to succeed. And now, most importantly, you will have the right tools.

Whether your overeating is caused by stress, anger, loneliness, anxiety, boredom, or any combination of the above, we can overcome this together. How would you feel if you lost 10 lbs? 20 lbs? 50 lbs? 100 lbs? Let's get to the root of the problem, and you'll see how much easier it is to lose weight.

And not just to lose the weight, but to keep it off. What use is it to lose twenty pounds if you just gain it back later? We want clear, sustainable results.

Keep reading and I'll teach you how to achieve the body you want.

# CHAPTER TWO

## The Diet is Broken

When you're succeeding at losing weight, the first thing anyone ever asks you is "What's your secret?"

What they really mean is "How do you make losing weight look so easy?" They're looking for a quick fix. They're looking for something that can be summed up easily in one or two sentences.

For instance, "I stopped eating meat," or, "I stopped eating sugar," are common quick fix solutions people try. Maybe you choose a more exotic plan and start trying juice fasts or extended, all-fruit diets. There are some extreme "secrets" out there.

Some people even find temporary relief with one of these extreme diets. They restrict food intake to certain groups, and they do shed a few pounds. I've known plenty of people who have cut sugars from their diet and lost some weight.

There are two problems with this approach, however. First of all, the "weight-loss secret" implies a sort of uniformity that doesn't really exist. Everybody is different and has different nutritional needs. Pretending there's a formula to follow for weight loss doesn't account for this wonderful diversity. This strategy focuses on the physical aspects of weight loss, instead of the emotional, which approaches the problem from the wrong angle. We all need to recognize that it's not about the food!

And in the long-term? After a few months, maybe a year, all the weight comes back. Now, of course, this isn't a foregone conclusion. Some people are able to pick a diet and stick to it. They adhere to the same rigid guidelines for years on end. For most people, however, the effects are only temporary.[8]

Diets seem appealing because they're simple, but they cause more harm than good. Anyone can diet. It's easy to try one out and see if there are positive results. In the long term, however, you're merely treating the symptoms of a much greater problem. Remember, it's not about the food.

There are three main challenges with dieting: rebellion, starvation, and focus on food. If you're an emotional overeater, I strongly suggest you avoid dieting. What should you do instead? We'll go over that in the next chapter.

## REBELLION

One of the biggest problems with dieting is the "rebellion" reaction.

Diets aren't natural—they have deprivation built into them. They take away something you enjoy. Addicted to potato chips or soda or bread? Diets are looking over your shoulder to make sure you don't eat any of them. The very idea of dieting means giving something up. It doesn't matter what, but you're going to have to abstain from eating something. That's the nature of a diet!

You start to feel deprived. Diets often trigger an "anti-authority" sentiment. Even though you're the only person enforcing your diet, you'll start to rebel against the responsible part of your brain. Like a surly teenager, you're going to become obstinate and refuse to "listen" to your diet eventually.

You'll begin to obsess about breaking your diet. You're going to feel desperate to get back to old habits of using food to soothe your feelings. Sooner or later, most people break their diets because diets aren't the solution. When you do, you'll feel guilty, and any progress will be erased.

Let's say you managed to stick to a diet for three weeks. You eat healthy foods and portions, you exercise regularly, and you start to see a positive change in your weight.

As the weeks go by, you start to feel better about yourself and believe you deserve a reward. Maybe you go out for a run one day and think, "I just exercised, so now I can cheat a bit and eat whatever I'd like."

Because it's been so long since the last time you treated yourself, you're not going to eat a *normal* meal. Instead, your feelings of deprivation will surface. You'll end up going way overboard, splurging on unhealthy food and undermining the progress you've made. You overeat in order to negate those latent feelings of deprivation, accumulated over the course of your diet.

If you're using a diet to curb your cravings, it's probably going to backfire. A diet actually enhances cravings over time. Because you deny yourself the food you want, the craving turns from a "want" into a "need." Stress from dieting triggers more cravings, and eventually it seems easier to just give in and eat the food to get rid of the craving. It doesn't matter how you justify it, it's still breaking your diet.

In fact, some people will actually gain *more* weight after a diet than they originally lost. The above example only deals with the ramifications of eating one splurge meal, but these feelings of deprivation often linger for a long time. Once you've cheated on one meal, you're more likely to keep cheating. In other words, after you break the diet the first time, it becomes exponentially harder to stay strong the next time around. You'll keep splurging on meals, potentially gaining back all the weight you originally lost and then some.

## STARVATION

A diet isn't really starvation, when done correctly. Your body is still supposed to get an appropriate amount of calories, though perhaps fewer than before. You might *feel* like you're starving, of course, but that's different than actual starvation. If you're on a diet unique to your body, taking into account your personal nutritional needs, you're probably doing fine.

Unfortunately, most people don't know much about nutrition, and dieting is one place where less isn't always more.

Counting calories doesn't tell the whole story, and you can't automatically assume that eating the smallest amount of calories possible will mean more weight loss. You see, when cutting calories, you eventually reach a point of diminishing returns. Your body is designed to keep itself alive, even during tough times. As such, you might even begin to *gain* weight if your diet program is too extreme.

If you eat too few calories, your body tries to compensate. You can't sit your body down and explain, "Hey, I'm going on a diet." It doesn't know or understand that you're trying your best to lose weight, and instead it actually starts to believe you're starving. Since your body considers starving "bad," it begins to panic. Instead of shedding all that unwanted weight, your body triggers an emergency mode where it hoards all the calories you eat and turns them into fat automatically instead of burning them off.

It's so frustrating. You *want* to burn the weight off. However, this "emergency mode" is an evolutionary response from ancient times when food was scarce. Your body thinks you are having trouble feeding yourself. In order to preserve enough energy for your organs to keep running, your body changes its hormonal composition. Your metabolism slows down, so you're burning fewer calories than you were before. This means you have to do even *more* to lose weight.

Anyone who wants to lose weight can recognize why this is a losing battle. It's already hard enough to lose weight when your metabolism is running at peak efficiency. Now imagine that it slows down and you keep putting on more weight even when you're eating a quarter of the calories!

Many people start off with a diet that is too extreme, and it comes back to haunt them. They start to complain about plateauing or gaining weight, and it's because their body has been disrupted by a near-starvation diet. This type of diet is easy to fall into when attempting to lose weight without the advice of a dietitian, and is one of the major problems with the dieting fad in our culture.

## THE FOCUS ON FOOD

By far the worst problem with traditional dieting is the portrayal of food as the problem. When we want to lose weight, we look first to the foods we eat before anything else.

Food is, admittedly, an easy target. We look at how many calories we're taking in and try to address that factor first. It's a concept that can be summed up easily. We think we understand how diets work, because we understand the math behind diets. Therefore, there's a lot of focus in our society on how many calories we're consuming and expending.

When it comes to dieting, you end up going through the same rituals each time—"I'm going on this diet, so I can't eat meat anymore," or maybe it's sugar, gluten, dairy, or any of the other standard targets. You focus all of your determination on avoiding that one type of food in order to limit your overall caloric intake.

But I have bad news. If you're an emotional overeater, it doesn't matter how many calories you count—your diet isn't going to work out. It's not for lack of trying. You're simply not examining the core reasons why you need to diet in the first place. Without addressing the emotional reasons underlying your excessive eating, you'll most likely fall back into old patterns of behavior at some point in the future because you haven't fully dealt with your underlying issues.

We don't overeat because we *want* to put on extra weight. It's not like we're all sitting around scarfing down chips and thinking, "Wow, I can't believe how healthy these potato chips are. I've made such a great decision!" We know it's bad for us. We all want to keep in shape, stay healthy, and live long and fulfilling lives, and we know the long-term problems caused by overeating. Still, we consistently overeat even though we know it's wrong.

Why?

Focusing on food choices doesn't address this baseline question of *why* we're overeating. It just tries to solve the problem on the surface. That's not helpful.

Food is a means to an end. Overeating is merely a symptom of a problem. Cutting back on food is like applying a Band-Aid as a quick fix. You might lose some weight in the short-term, but the same struggles are going to manifest in a different way eventually.

To permanently stop *over*eating, we need to delve deeper into our emotions. We need to address the root of the problem, instead of trying to bandage it up. You're eating because you want to numb difficult emotions, because you're bored or distracted, because you're tired and stressed. You're eating, in other words, because something is driving you to use food to avoid painful emotions.

Doesn't it make sense to go straight to the cause of your bad habits instead of making surface attempts to change? You're going to feel so much better in the long-term. Once you've addressed the core issues, you can lose the weight and keep it off. No more of this yo-yo effect, where you lose it and then gain it back sooner or later. No more starvation diets.

If you can soothe your inner fears, confront the emotions you've been trying to numb with food, and change your bad habits, you can stop overeating *forever*.

This approach is at the core of my book: address the emotions, not the food.

People's bodies vary. Some people may eat a 2,000 calorie diet and lose weight, others might follow the same diet and gain weight. It's impossible to know what your personal situation is. Focusing on the food won't change your habits or your weight for long.

I know why you overeat— some of your emotions are upsetting and challenging. I may not know the specific event or emotions that cause you to overeat, but I do know how to help you feel better and teach you to no longer use food for the "wrong" reasons. I know how to help you eliminate your emotionally-driven cravings in a healthy, constructive manner.

I've worked with thousands of clients during my career, and helping them overcome emotional overeating is immensely rewarding. There's a real, noticeable benefit to healing destructive eating habits—and it's easy to tell when this approach is working because my clients start losing weight without having to force themselves into some sort of diet or deprive themselves of their favorite foods.

Instead, they simply become less interested in those high caloric junk foods and less obsessed with eating to suppress or numb their emotions.

The secret is known as Emotional Freedom Techniques, or EFT—most commonly known as "Tapping."

# CHAPTER THREE

## Introducing EFT

Earlier in my career, I helped people overcome all sorts of obstacles using the knowledge acquired from my doctorate in Clinical Hypnotherapy. Hypnosis can be a powerful tool, when used properly and consistently. For example, I've helped clients feel more relaxed or break their smoking habit.

But I just could not get hypnosis to work for any extended amount of time when it came to weight loss. It wasn't for lack of trying. Due to my hypnosis background, client after client would seek out my services to help them lose weight.

I'd get these calls from people desperate to lose weight. They'd heard hypnosis could potentially help them. They'd admit to feeling utterly helpless, as if they had no control over their habits. They said they could lose weight, yes. Then they'd put all the weight back on. They were trapped in this yo-yo cycle, and they couldn't do anything about it. Dieting wasn't working. They needed further support.

So we'd try hypnosis.

Unfortunately, my results with hypnosis and weight loss were spotty, at best. I'd used hypnosis to break other types of addictions, but overeating was not responding consistently. Some clients would "forget" to do their homework in between sessions. Other clients would simply stop showing up to therapy sessions, or keep overeating and sabotage the work we were doing. Hypnosis was not helping them enough to make a permanent change in their lifestyle.

I did have a few success cases using hypnosis with weight loss clients. On the whole, however, I became discouraged with the weight loss segment of the market. I didn't feel hypnosis was enough or that I could give those clients the help they deserved; I couldn't guarantee them results. It wasn't fair for them, and it was causing me a lot of stress. I promised myself I wouldn't work with any more weight loss clients until I found the right tool to do so in a reliable, efficient manner.

Before we discuss this tool, I want to give you a quick background on the underlying issue in emotional overeating: Stress.

I think a brief discussion of the mechanics of stress is a good idea at this point because it has a lot to do with you choices about emotional overeating. When we think about something stressful in our lives, it automatically triggers the amygdala in our brain (our "smoke alarm") to register that there is danger lurking somewhere. It doesn't matter whether we're thinking about work, a relationship, our body, or our family, it immediately triggers the "fight-or-flight" response, which sends a series of stress hormones such as cortisol and adrenaline through our bodies.

When this happens it is completely normal to want to over-eat to calm yourself down, if that's what you are accustomed to doing when you feel stress. It's an automatic reaction, and you likely have little control over it once it gets triggered. Here's where tapping helps to interrupt this cycle.

Tapping seems to neutralize this automatic reaction in-side of your brain, allowing you to think more clearly and make different decisions. Tapping seems to interrupt your interpretation or perception of danger, sending a calming response through your body. In fact, in certain research studies, Tapping has been shown to lower the levels of cortisol in your bloodstream.

This is all good news. When you lower your reaction to stress and interrupt the flight-or-fight reaction in your body and mind, you no longer feel compelled to use food to calm your emotions. This is why I recommend using the Tapping sequences during extremely stressful times, and throughout your day, not just when you are hit by sudden cravings.

I discovered this tool in the late nineties.

In 1997 I began learning a "tapping" method from Dr. Fred Gallo, a psychologist who had studied with Dr. Roger Callahan.[9] Dr. Callahan founded the entire field now called "Tapping." His particular brand was called TFT, or Thought Field Therapy, which featured this tapping method as a core tenet. I was originally drawn towards TFT because I felt compelled to broaden my horizons and take on new challenges.

Shortly after learning the basics of TFT, I learned of the work of Gary Craig.[10] Craig founded a complementary Tapping treatment program known as EFT, or Emotional Freedom Techniques. I began working extensively with Craig's simplified tapping method, EFT. EFT had much in common with TFT, but streamlined the tapping technique I'd been studying under Dr. Gallo. EFT is the tool I've dedicated myself to for more than 15 years, and the one that helps my clients get the most satisfying results.

I know EFT works because I've seen its effects on me and countless others. It's the best tool I've found for helping my clients, and one that I strongly recommend to anyone struggling with any number of emotionally-based issues.

In a practical sense, EFT is the tool we're going to use to address your emotional overeating. When I first began experimenting with EFT I noticed it was far more powerful at addressing root issues in addictions than hypnotherapy. I was having consistent, quick success helping people break their smoking addictions, and I began to wonder just how powerful this tool really was.

I started to experiment with a combination of hypnotherapy and EFT. Not only did I notice changes in my clients' behavior, but my own behavior as well! I found my stress-related food cravings relaxed considerably.

I kept experimenting with Tapping for weight loss. I'd routinely land on new, exciting ways to approach weight loss with EFT. Eventually, I felt like I'd figured out a consistent plan that could help emotional overeaters turn the corner and lose the weight once and for all. I started to demonstrate consistent, healthy results with weight loss clients.

When you focus on food in a diet, you come up against this wall: everyone is different. With EFT, however, I was able to lay out a plan that worked. While each person required a modicum of individualization, there were definite themes and patterns I found I could work with time and time again to help people overcome their tendencies to overeat. That plan is the blueprint for this book.

I'm going to really dive into EFT ("Tapping") in the next chapter. I'll explain to you on a step-by-step basis how it works and how to implement it in your life. First I will give you an overview and history of the technique.

Please forgive me if you've read one of my other books before or have worked with Tapping in your own life, as a lot of this information may seem repetitive or incredibly basic. If you do have experience with Tapping, I suggest you skip this chapter and move on to the next section. However, if you've never worked with EFT before, I firmly believe this chapter will be a huge help.

At its core, I like to say Meridian Tapping (the central mechanic of EFT) is "emotional acupuncture." Now don't worry! It's not real acupuncture, and there aren't any needles involved in the process.

Nevertheless, emotional acupuncture is a very illuminating image, is it not? We're not going to use needles to accomplish our goals, but we are working with the same system of energy. In fact, if you've ever studied or tried acupuncture you'll probably recognize the standard "meridian" structure in Tapping.

The meridians are channels that route energy throughout the human body. The meridian system is an ancient Chinese concept, developed over four thousand years ago and still used in modern times. A healthy meridian is clear or unblocked, and helps keep the body and mind in perpetual balance.

Life energy, or "chi," flows through the meridians, these channels in our body. When the meridians are kept clear, the stream of chi travels freely through our system. An unrestricted flow of chi is indispensable to a healthy human body, and unblocked meridians are essential to this process.

Think of the meridians, for instance, as arteries and veins, providing safe conduct for energy instead of blood. When we have a blockage in our cardiovascular system, we recognize it as a health issue. We try to take blood thinners or break up clots. A blockage in our meridians can also cause health problems, both mentally and physically, and is something we must address as soon as possible.

Acupuncture is one method for treating the flow of your energy. Correct application of acupuncture needles will resume the flow of chi in your meridians, repairing any problems in the process.

On the other hand, acupuncture is a delicate art. It requires years of study and dedication to memorize and understand the interaction of hundreds of acupuncture points in the human body, so it's not exactly approachable for the layperson. Plus, I'm not really a fan of needles, and I assume you aren't either.

And that's why I prefer EFT or tapping on meridian points. Tapping, as used when conducting an EFT session, adapts the basic tenets of acupuncture without the complexity or the needles. The theory in Tapping, like acupuncture, firmly believes that our mental, physical, and emotional health relies on a clear and unrestricted flow of chi through our meridians. This theory, borrowed from Ancient Chinese Medicine, says we can trace all of our problems in life back to blocked meridians. Fix the blockage and we address the root of the issue.

But Tapping is not acupuncture. Tapping is something you can use even if you're a novice in the field of energy medicine, or just learned about EFT through this book. It doesn't matter who you are. You could be a parent, a student, a businessperson, a musician, an artist, an engineer—we all have meridians, and we can all benefit from the healthy flow of energy enhanced by regular Tapping.

Even after just a few minutes of EFT, countless people notice a difference in their emotional outlook. Tapping is quick. Tapping is painless. Tapping is absolutely the best solution I've found in over 22 years in the mental health field to heal your emotional overeating. I've never met a single client who didn't start seeing results almost immediately when they put real effort into using EFT. This is a powerful technique that I've seen work for cravings, plateaus, stress, body shame, and relapse.

And as if that weren't enough, EFT is much easier than most other tools you might use.

Let's start with the basics: the meridians. In EFT we only focus on nine meridian points. Nine points isn't that bad, right? Don't worry about what to do with those points. Throughout the next few chapters I'm going to teach you how to reach your maximum potential with Tapping. I'll teach you how to tap efficiently, how hard or soft to tap, and the phrases you'll say along the way to reinforce the physical tapping.

This book is a complete how-to guide for using Tapping for your personal benefit. You're going to learn to address your emotional overeating, obviously, but the technique you'll learn over the course of this book could just as easily be applied to fixing your tendency to procrastinate, for instance. Once you've used EFT to solve one problem in your life, you'll want to use it to solve a whole range of issues, and you can! That's what amazes me about EFT even 17 years after I learned how to use it—it's applicable for such a broad spectrum of problems.

I know there's a lot of vocabulary in this chapter you might be unfamiliar with, or may have heard but never seen implemented. If you're feeling overwhelmed, I want to reassure you: by the time you've finished this book, you'll have a full understanding of all the concepts of EFT and Meridian Tapping, and you'll be able to put them into practice. This chapter is solely to provide you with the terminology we'll be using later on in the book.

The program in this book will help you in two distinct ways – by lowering your resistance and raising your vibration. On the one hand, we want to lower your "resistance" which consists of all the negative feelings you store—feelings like fear, loneliness, apathy, or stress.

The other way this book will help you is to raise your "vibration." Simply put, vibration is our mood. When we raise our vibration, we become more willing to notice abundance and the things we appreciate in our life. When you focus on positive thinking and take time to notice the positive aspects of life, you have a higher vibration than someone who is always pessimistic about the future. That's not to say maintaining a positive outlook is easy, or that you'll never slip up. Life can be hard, and it's easy to fall into old, negative ways of thinking if you're not vigilant.

It's likely you'll start to notice a difference after just a few short sessions of EFT.

I've seen this work in numerous contexts. I first used EFT to help address my horrible procrastination habits. I knew procrastination, rooted in fear and doubt about my own success, was holding me back in both my career and my personal life, and I resolved to overcome it. I started to use Tapping on a regular basis, a little bit every day. I targeted the negative emotions prolonging my bad habits and worked to move past that old baggage.

I did it! I eliminated every vestige of a lifelong procrastination problem and allowed myself to move forward in life. The results were better than I ever dreamed possible prior to studying EFT. I increased both my personal satisfaction and my income by eliminating procrastination.

Once I'd seen the results of EFT on my procrastination, I decided to broaden my horizons. I applied the same techniques to other issues, such as my insomnia, and I started sleeping normally again. After that I became a true believer. I relieved chronic pains, cleared up strong anxiety, and eliminated a lot of long-held negative emotion.

Once I started testing the waters with EFT, I realized how much more powerful it was than hypnotherapy. I began experimenting with EFT and my own food cravings, doing a few tests with both my own appetite and a small cluster of clients.

I was amazed at how effective EFT was when applied to cravings and the underlying emotions that drive people to overeat. I learned how to target the primary emotions of overeating habits, which was the key to eliminating the problem.

After experimenting with EFT and witnessing clear, consistent results, I immediately started helping my clients with the techniques I'd learned —the same techniques I'm teaching you in this book. This isn't the "lite" version of my program. The only advantage I have over you is experience, and that comes with practice. I'm going to teach you how to use EFT because I *know* it can bring you relief. Emotional overeating is an exasperating habit —one that affects far too many people. The more I can do to help, the better.

# CHAPTER FOUR

## Implementing EFT

I know how frustrating the cycle of emotional overeating can be. Because of EFT, it's been many years since I've really worried about my weight and food cravings, but I still remember how it felt to struggle against my own body, fighting those powerful food cravings, due to stressors in my life. I hated losing control. It was humiliating.

And all that time I was working against myself. I thought if I just found the right diet, or exercised a bit more, everything would work out. I thought eventually I'd make a breakthrough of some kind and start seeing results. I had the right goal in mind, but I had no real idea how to accomplish it.

I've been where you are. I know how it feels.

The good news is we can move past this together. All I need from you is effort and cooperation.

What would you give to get rid of your food cravings? What would you give to go into your kitchen and think, "You know, I'm not really hungry right now. Maybe later," and then walk out again? What would you give to lose the extra pounds once and for all?

You deserve that. You deserve to take control of your body and mind again. Starting in this chapter, I'm going to teach you how to make that goal a reality. Using EFT, we're going to get rid of those pesky cravings and the mindless overeating that prevents you from losing weight permanently. All you need to do to be successful is to follow the four steps in this chapter.

I've said it before and I'll say it again: I love EFT ("Tapping") because it's so easy to learn and use. I've had over 15 years of experience with EFT and I'm highly skilled when using it on my clients, but EFT is amazing because even a newcomer to the technique can make significant progress. You can come to this book with absolutely zero knowledge of Tapping and finish feeling confident you will achieve clear goals in your life. I haven't found any other tool as potent as Tapping that can create similar results.

Additionally, once you know EFT, you really *know* EFT. I said earlier I used EFT to help clear my procrastination, my insomnia, and my food cravings. That's just a small subset of the issues I've used EFT for with my clients. Any bad habits and emotional conflicts you've picked up over the years can likely be worked through using the same EFT training you're about to learn in this book.

EFT is simply the most effective tool I've found for permanent change. I've put in the time to try out other programs. I have a Master's Degree in Clinical Social Work, and a degree in Clinical Hypnotherapy. In the past I tried many techniques to better help my clients, and I've stuck with EFT because I know it provides the most impressive results. I've seen what EFT can do.

With EFT you get results in a timely manner. Some other tools and programs I've worked with are completely ineffective, while others succeed eventually, but the time commitment is far too high. Hypnotherapy could technically get rid of your emotional overeating, given enough time, but it doesn't eradicate the cause—the struggle to avoid emotions—and most people will give up on the process long before they achieve the long-term results they desire.

Now that's not to say EFT is going to be easy, or require no effort on your part. You need to be a willing and active participant in order to experience success, and you're going to need to keep up a routine even after your initial positive results. It's easy to start making a change, but you need to keep up with using this tool if you want to meet your goals. You'll want to keep practicing EFT on a daily basis to achieve results.

But follow my instructions, put in the effort, and you will see exciting results. I can guarantee it.

As I said earlier, using EFT is easy compared to other tools. The basic components of EFT are simple to remember: nine meridian points, tapping, and repeating phrases out loud. That's it. That's all you need to do to use this Tapping program. For such a powerful technique, it's amazing how simple the actual process is.

I hope you remember some of what we discussed in the last chapter. It will come in handy in this chapter, as we go over the actual steps involved in EFT. All of the background knowledge on Meridian Tapping will play into the process I describe in this chapter.

If you still feel a bit fuzzy on some of the terms, don't worry! I'll try to keep it easy to follow. I know there's a lot of vocabulary involved, and I hope I avoid overwhelming anyone.

So now let's go over technique. I've given you all the background information you need to understand EFT on a theoretical level. All that remains are the physical motions and verbal phrases involved. I've broken the entire process down into four steps. Each step builds off the previous one, so no skipping ahead!

You will start by choosing a "target."

## STEP ONE: CHOOSING A TARGET

Choosing a target is actually an easy task for you. Why? Because in large part, by picking up this book you've already done it.

The first step in EFT, choosing a target, means deciding what emotion or habit you want to focus on when using Tapping.

Since you've picked up this book, I think it's safe to say your overall target is emotional overeating. We want to eventually solve the root of your food cravings and understand what pulls you towards habitual overeating.

"Root" is the key word here, though. Your *overall* target is emotional overeating, but that's quite a hefty goal. It's fine as a launching off point, but not exactly the most efficient way to address your bad habits. There may be two or more emotions or stressors contributing to your overeating habit, even if you don't know it yet. Divide and conquer is an excellent strategy in EFT. Figure out and attack each of the root causes (emotions) individually, rather than focusing on the behavior of emotional overeating as a general concept.

We want to dig deeper into the cause of your overeating. Taking on the entirety of your overeating habit at once is making more work for yourself and may be overwhelming. EFT works because of a key component, and it's right there in the formal name – Emotional Freedom Techniques—*emotion*. We need to know what the root emotion is that's causing you to overeat, or procrastinate, or smoke cigarettes, or to choose any of these bad habits you've picked up over the years.

Overeating? There's no specific emotion tied to overeating across the board for *everyone*. It's personal. There are specific emotions *you* feel that cause you to eat too much or too often. I always ate over stress and worry. You may overeat because of fear or loneliness.

Now remember, there are also emotions that your overeating leads you to experience. Perhaps you eat too much and feel ashamed, disgusted, or angry at yourself. These emotions are tied to overeating, in that they occur after that habit, but they're also not the root causes. We don't want to treat the emotions overeating causes us to feel *afterward*. ***We want to treat the emotions causing us to overeat in the first place.*** Make sense?

Let's start on an extremely basic level.

When I introduce clients to EFT ("Tapping"), I often ask them to focus on one of three things: an emotion, a symptom, or an event. Now, in the long run you're actually going to relate everything back to an emotion. If you decide to focus on a symptom you'll want to know what emotion is related to that symptom. Why do you feel afraid when thinking of that symptom, for instance? The same goes for events. You want to know what negative emotion you've tied to that event—fear, anger, or loneliness, for example. Focusing on an emotion means you'd be targeting anger, or hurt, or loneliness. Focusing on a symptom might mean targeting your cravings. While focusing on an event might mean zeroing in on one upsetting time in your life when you resorted to using food in a crisis to help make you feel better.

For instance, I had a client who overate repeatedly because her boss treated her poorly. She kept getting so stressed out because of her boss's mistreatment that she'd come home and just eat most of the night away. When we started working on her habit of overeating it was useful for her to focus on that day's conflicts with her boss and the emotions that came along with it, whether stress, anger, or frustration.

As I said, it's perfectly acceptable for you to begin using EFT with only "emotional overeating" as your target. Just realize you're probably going to want to change your target to something more specific such as "stress" or "fear" or "anger."

And as you start to use Tapping, you will eventually get more in touch with the emotional roots of any problems you experience. EFT is an excellent tool because it's very fluid and dynamic. As you work with a target, you'll naturally find yourself digging deeper into the problem and recognizing those emotional causes, even if you couldn't think of them at the beginning. Tapping helps you get in touch with your emotions, which in turn helps you get better at targeting the root causes of your problems. It's a win-win.

For right now, I'd recommend referring to my earlier discussion about the different types of emotional overeating. Perhaps rereading that section will trigger something in your mind and allow you to analyze your own habits and decide which specific emotion seems to trigger your overeating.

Do you overeat because of stress? That's already a better target to focus on than the general topic of the behavior of "overeating." We can understand stress. We can address stress head-on. Stress is something universal. Everyone has experienced it. Stress makes a great target in EFT, because we can all feel it in our bodies and our minds. You can concentrate on what the feeling of stress means to you, and then try to clear those negative emotions with Tapping. Eliminate stress and you eliminate the cause of your emotional overeating. Sounds simple, right?

Plus there are all sorts of residual benefits. You're not just eliminating the stress connected with your emotional overeating, you're increasing your ability to handle all stress. You're calming your entire body and mind. You'll be able to function better in both your personal and professional life, simply because you wanted to get rid of your overeating habits.

The same goes for any emotion you might choose to target. Are you overeating because you're angry? Lonely? Any of these make a more compelling target than simply concentrating on overeating as a whole.

I want to address what causes you to overeat in the first place—these deeply hidden emotions at the core of your overeating habit. The more you *feel* those emotions, the better the tapping process will work for you. The process responds better when you are tuned into these powerful emotions.

Here are some additional questions you may want to ask yourself to help identify the core emotions you use food to avoid:

When do you typically overeat?

How do you feel when you are overeating?

Why do you think you eat when you're not hungry?

What feelings are you afraid might surface if you can't overeat?

Do you feel deprived of time, money, or love?

What would be the "downside" to losing weight?

Does being overweight "serve" you in any way? Protect you?

Eventually you'll be able to reduce any problematic behavior down to an emotional core. I hope once you've conquered your emotional overeating habit you'll introduce EFT into other aspects of your life. Tapping can help you overcome so many obstacles. I've already discussed procrastination and smoking, but EFT is versatile enough to work on practically any negative behavior or feeling you want to overcome, such as fear of success, fear of failure, or self confidence issues. You owe it to yourself to keep working with Tapping even after you've addressed these immediate issues.

To summarize: pick an emotion (e.g., fear), a symptom (a craving), or an event (the time your mother yelled at you) you want to focus on healing. Be open and honest with yourself. Let yourself identify and feel the root emotions, if you can find them.

## STEP TWO: RATING

We'll get to Tapping shortly, but there are still some administrative tasks to take care of when using EFT. Before we move forward, I need you to rate your feelings towards the target. This will come in handy later as we try to determine whether EFT is having a positive effect on you or not. In this program I use a simple zero-to-ten point scale. Zero represents the least severe reaction towards your target, and ten the most intense.

What do I mean? Let me try to break it down a bit more.

Right now I want you to focus on the target you chose back in step one. Clear your mind except for the thought of the target—let's say the feeling of fear. Now how high is this feeling on the zero-to-ten point scale?

Or, as I like to say, how *much* do you feel?

Your target is made up of an emotion, or negative energy, so focusing on it will cause you discomfort or distress. This response is what you're measuring. How uncomfortable do you feel when you sit and think about your target?

In step one I said it's important that your target, even if it's an event or symptom, has an emotional root. This rating process is the reason why. It's perfectly fine to use overeating as a target in theory, but you need to be able to rate the severity of your emotional response. This rating system is the key to assessing whether your EFT session is successful or not. It's the only way I know to measure whether or not you're making real progress.

You're going to use this rating method before and after every EFT session. If you've chosen a target with little emotion, you won't notice much change when you measure your feeling with the rating system. You can then choose to restart the process with a clearer target in mind, or refine your original target. It's no use expending energy and time on a target that isn't clear or doesn't express the truth for you. You'll only get frustrated by the lack of results. It's much better to simply revisit step one in search of a better target.

Let's do it for real this time. Get somewhere quiet and comfortable, if possible. Concentrate fully on the target you've chosen from step one (a feeling, a symptom, or the memory of an event). Poke and prod at it as if it were a toothache you are unable to ignore; explore how it makes you feel.

Then rate your response on the zero-to-ten point scale. Remember, zero is the least severe response and ten is the most severe.

Eventually, you want to reduce your rating down to zero or as close as possible. It might take multiple sessions to get there, or you might *never* get to zero. A zero rating means you've completely eliminated the negative feeling that was your target; this may be unfeasible. You may get down to a one or two and then hit a plateau. That's also totally fine. A rating of one or two means the emotion has a negligible effect on your everyday life; you should be able to manage the emotion at that level.

If, on the other hand, your initial rating and discomfort is already close to the low end of the spectrum—say, between zero and two—then the target you've chosen isn't actually the main issue in your life. You might have *thought* it was an issue, but this test has shown that there's a more fundamental issue causing you pain. I recommend revisiting step one and choosing a new feeling as a target.

I always tell clients when they start this rating process: don't worry about what *other* people would say. Don't rate your discomfort level against some imaginary "objective" discomfort. Someone out there might have it worse than you, but this isn't a comparison. Focus entirely on your own feelings. If you feel like your overeating is an enormous problem in *your* life, then that's an entirely valid response and you're more than welcome to rate it a ten. These numbers don't necessarily mean anything, outside of your personal reaction.

I simply want a way to quantify your results in a way you can readily refer to later. I want you to be able to look back after a session and say, "Today I brought my ten down to a six," or, "Today I brought the emotions underlying my overeating from a seven down to a two." These are results you can point to directly and *know* that EFT is helping you work through any underlying problems. There's no guesswork involved.

Even if an emotion goes down to zero, it might not stay there. You could check your emotions a few weeks later and think, "Oh, that zero has gone back up to a four or five." This simply means another aspect of the problem has surfaced, or more stress in your life has retriggered your cravings or behavior. The good news is you'll know how to face your negative emotions the next time around, and that's much more than you could have said before.

Once you choose your target and it's properly rated, you're ready for the next step!

## STEP THREE: THE SETUP STATEMENT

I've worked with thousands of clients over the years individually and in groups, helping introduce them to EFT. No matter what, the setup statement is always the hardest part to grasp for newcomers because everyone makes it more complicated than it needs to be. Right up front I want to warn you not to get discouraged if the first few setup statements you make don't provide the amazing results you hoped for with this new tool. I promise if you stick with it you'll get better with time, until eventually creating a setup statement becomes second nature to you.

The setup statement is one of the most important parts of EFT. It's the formula we use to identify our target and reduce our resistance through self-acceptance.

The basic guidelines for the setup statement haven't changed since EFT was first developed. There are two main parts we need to combine: naming the problem, and then combining it with an affirmation of acceptance.

Here's an example of the basic format:

"Even though I feel really stressed out, I deeply and profoundly love and accept myself anyway."

Notice the two parts. The first half of the setup statement names the problem you're focusing on, while the second half affirms that you love and accept yourself in spite of this challenge. It is a part of you, you acknowledge and accept it, and you're willing to change.

Let's set up the first half. You need to name the problem you're focusing on. Luckily, you already did that! The problem you're working on is the target you came up with back in step one (the feeling of stress, a craving, or a memory of a negative event.) Just make a note of the target for now.

You're going to join the target to the second half of the sentence, the statement of acceptance. This second half is important because it allows you to start the healing process. You want to acknowledge that you accept yourself no matter what issue you've chosen to focus on—in this case overeating, but really any symptom, emotion, or event you've identified as a target—because it allows you to release the constant self-hatred you have about this issue. You need to be okay with who you *are* right now before you can become the person you aspire to be.

The second half of the statement tends to follow a particular format. For instance, "I deeply and profoundly love and accept who I am and how I feel," or, "I deeply appreciate every part of myself," or, "I deeply and profoundly love and accept myself anyway." Anything along those lines will fulfill the same purpose.

I love the format of the setup statement. It's simple and elegant. You're following the same basic form every time—naming the problem and combining it with an expression of acceptance.

The setup statement is so poignant because you're naming one of the things you dislike or fear most about yourself and immediately pointing out how much love you hold for yourself, regardless. It's a wonderful sentiment that builds self-respect.

Acceptance is the *key* to the setup statement. If you isolate the first half of the statement it might look negative. You're focusing on this flaw in yourself. However, take both halves as a whole and it's clear the setup statement is overall a positive force. You're inviting positive energy into your life by accepting yourself even while acknowledging your flaws. You're not holding yourself back by trying to fight against your problems. Instead, you're allowing self-acceptance to heal these problems.

As simple as the setup statement seems, there's a lot of room for variation. Everyone's setup statement looks slightly different, and it might take you a few sessions before you feel comfortable with the concept. You're going to find some statements more effective than others, and your preferences might change over time, as you become more comfortable or experienced using EFT. Even in the middle of a session you might find yourself refining your setup statement. This is normal and to be expected.

For instance, if your emotional overeating arises from anger, your setup statement may look something like:

"Even though I automatically reach for food every time I'm angry, I deeply and profoundly love and accept myself anyway,"

"Even though food has always made me feel calmer when I'm angry, I appreciate every aspect of myself anyway."

We'll go over more of these variations in a later chapter, where I will provide you with some concrete examples of setup statements to use in a number of situations. If you're just starting off, or even if you've used EFT before, you're welcome to take those examples and roll them into your personal program. I provide them in hopes they'll inspire you to delve deeper into the power of EFT. Feel free to use the examples I've provided if you think they'll get you closer to your goal.

How will you know whether the Tapping is helping you or not? This is where the rating system comes into play. If you've gone through a few sessions with a certain setup statement and aren't making progress, it's time to revisit your target or setup statement and decide if there's a way to improve on it.

Don't worry if you feel stuck. The setup statement, as I said, is a challenging part of EFT *because* it's so crucial. The formula is deceptively simple. You might feel like you've got the perfect setup statement and then after a few sessions you realize you've made zero progress. With years of experience I can say creating a good setup statement is challenging because it's so personalized. Everyone's situation is different, and it can be hard to land on the exact right words to make the most of EFT. Remember, the most important point is to tell the "truth" in the setup statement.

Luckily, you should be able to make some progress simply by using the statements in this book. They're more generalized than if you made your own setup statement, but you'll at least get a feel for the form as you practice. Really, that's the heart of it: keep practicing! You'll get better with experience.

And whatever you do, make sure you go into the next step with a setup statement ready. You cannot skip or skimp on the setup statement. It is *vital* to the success of the program as you move into the tapping phase.

## STEP FOUR: TAPPING

Here we reach the core of the EFT program: tapping on the meridian points. Tapping is, as I said earlier, "emotional acupuncture." It follows the same principles as acupuncture, without any of the needles. Now that you have your target, rating, and setup statement, you're ready to start working directly with the nine meridian points and clearing your energy system. While the setup statement in particular is vital to the success of EFT, the tapping process is where you really start to heal your negative emotions.

Your first few Tapping sessions with a particular target may be quite dramatic. Since you've never worked directly with the negative emotions underlying your overeating before, there's a chance you'll experience pretty good results—from a ten down to a five, for instance. These are, relatively speaking, large drops in negative energy.

Later on, when you're working primarily on preventative EFT for maintenance, your sessions may take a mere ten to fifteen minutes. It doesn't take as much effort to bring your emotions down from a four to a two before continuing about your day, for example.

Before you begin the Tapping, I want you to look at your surroundings. Like any meditative exercise, EFT functions best if you find a quiet, calm area where you can remain focused over the course of the session. EFT requires you to concentrate deeply on your target, and distractions will render the process less effective and diminish your results. Your attention is vital to the success of the program.

Emotional acupuncture is an evocative term, but what does it really mean?

Over the years I've developed an analogy I think best describes to new clients what is actually happening while practicing Tapping.

Imagine your brain is a computer. In fact, you don't have to really imagine. Your brain has a lot in common with an immensely complex and advanced computer. It's a filing system for all of your thoughts and memories. Somewhere in your brain is a file or document about whatever target you focused on in step one of this guide. For instance, there's a file called "emotional overeating" somewhere in your brain. Pretend you've just "opened" the document on emotional overeating. Inside are all the reasons you overeat, the emotions that drive you to overeat, and the feelings of hating yourself for it.

Tapping *edits* this file, almost like you opened a text file on your computer and corrected several sentences. Focusing your brain on the file during Tapping is what allows you to do this editing. When you've completed a Tapping session, hopefully the file has been altered to include more positive thoughts.

With this example, hopefully you can see why it's so important to remain focused on the target during the Tapping. Without concentrating on the file, you're essentially doing nothing to change your actual emotions. You might *look* like you're Tapping successfully, but you'll end a session and rate your discomfort a second time and find it hasn't changed. You're not getting any of the benefits of Tapping, at least in terms of that specific target. There's always a bit of change because your meridians will open up, but you need to be focused on a target to make any headway.

So stay focused! It's key to the whole process. I can't emphasize that enough.

The most important aspect of Meridian Tapping is choosing a specific target and staying focused while you use Tapping.

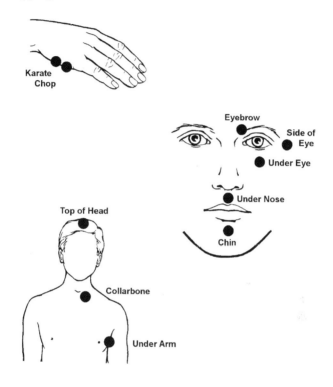

The first point of contact is the **Karate Chop Point.**

The Karate Chop Point is the fleshy part on the outside of your hand, between your wrist and your pinky. If you've seen any martial arts movies, it's the part an old Karate master would use to break through a board. That's where you want to tap initially.

A point of clarification: it doesn't matter which hand you use to tap, whether you prefer left or right is a purely personal decision, based on whichever feels comfortable. I'm right-handed, so I use the fingers on my right hand to tap on the Karate Chop Point on my left hand, but it works equally well either way.

I hope you have your setup statement ready, because it's now time to use it. Remember, Tapping is only part of what makes EFT so successful.

As you're tapping on your Karate Chop Point, I want you to say your setup statement three times. For instance, let's use one of the setup statements from the last section. If you overeat because you're angry, you would tap on the Karate Chop Point while repeating "Even though food has always made me feel calmer when angry, I appreciate every aspect of myself anyway," three times.

Think of this like opening that file on your computer. The setup statement primes your brain to receive the effects of the Tapping by allowing you to focus on the target. I wasn't kidding when I said the setup statement is crucial to the success of EFT. The setup statement is basically the foundation on which the Tapping process stands. A successful setup statement gets you ready to rewrite those bad habits. You're telling your brain "Listen up; this is our focus for this EFT session." The file opens, and you're ready to move on to the next meridian point. A vague setup statement fails to provide you with the necessary focus needed to continue.

This routine—tapping on the Karate Chop Point while repeating the setup statement three times—occurs each time you revise your problem, as a way to refocus the brain on the task ahead.

But there is a sequence of nine meridian points in the EFT program, and the Karate Chop Point is only the first. Once you've repeated your setup statement three times while tapping on the fleshy part of your hand, you're ready to proceed to the subsequent meridian points.

With these points, I recommend tapping with two fingers. As always, it doesn't matter whether you use your right or left hand, or tap on the left or right side of your face and body, as long as you're comfortable.

Many of my clients ask me how fast they're supposed to go. Simply keep a moderate, steady pace. I'd estimate my own tapping at approximately twice per second, but it doesn't matter as long as you don't feel lethargic or rushed. Don't think about it! Find a comfortable rhythm and settle on it.

Tapping is a way to reset the energy flowing through your body, but it takes surprisingly little force to do so. Tap firmly, but not hard. Tapping is effective because of the way your fingers make contact with points on your body, not because you have to physically break up any blocked meridians. Please don't hurt yourself!

The setup statement primed your brain to call up the "emotional overeating" file, or whatever target you've chosen to work on. However, it's *hard* to stay focused on a single thought for any period of time, even if you know it's essential to getting the most out of your sessions, so EFT incorporates what we call "reminder phrases."

A reminder phrase is something we say every time we tap on a new meridian point. It's a simple phrase that simply reminds us of the problem. By restating the problem while tapping we keep the target called up in our minds and get better results from each session.

Since the reminder phrase just names the problem again, it's akin to saying the first half of the setup statement without continuing on to the second half. Let me give an example.

A setup statement might say something like:

"Even though food has always made me feel calmer when I'm angry, I appreciate every aspect of myself anyway."

The reminder phrase cuts out the affirmation in the second half. It would look something like:

"Food makes me feel calm when I'm angry."

The reminder phrase can change at each new point, if you'd like—you could say, "Food makes me feel calm when I'm angry" eight times in a row, or you might say it the first time, and then change it to, "My anger causes me to overeat," the second time, and, "I overeat because I'm angry," the third time. Each reminder phrase is related, but can be unique. This helps keep you focused, ensuring you're not mindlessly repeating the same phrase. I've included more examples of reminder phrases in the next chapter, if you need further help.

The setup statement is essential because it helps you call up the file and begin the process of editing your emotions. Repeating the reminder phrase each time helps you alleviate the discomfort the target causes you to feel, continuing the process. The reminder phrase also helps you dig deeper into the root of the problem, perhaps opening up new emotional avenues to explore in later EFT sessions.

You've tapped on the Karate Chop Point, repeated your setup statement three times, and you know you need to repeat a reminder phrase. At this point, you're ready to begin tapping on the rest of the acupuncture points in the EFT program.

The next acupuncture point is located right above your nose, at the beginning of your eyebrow. It's not your third eye point (if you're familiar with that concept). This point is quite literally at the beginning of one of your eyebrows.

As always, EFT doesn't care whether you prefer your left or right side. Use whichever eyebrow you feel most comfortable using.

Tap on your eyebrow point firmly, with a constant rhythm, and try to concentrate completely on your target. Still thinking about your target while you *continue to tap,* say your reminder phrase out loud ("*Food helps me calm down when I'm angry*").

Continuing with our earlier example, you might say, "I overeat because I'm angry," as you tap on your eyebrow point. Saying the reminder phrase out loud keeps you focused on the target and draws you closer to your emotions, allowing the editing process to take place.

This is the basic routine you'll follow at each of the subsequent meridian points. Not too bad, right?

The next point is located at the outside corner of the eye. Make sure you stay right at the corner! I've seen some clients tapping as far back as their temple, and that's too far. Aim for the boney section next to where your eyelids come together. Once again, you want to tap on this point and repeat your (perhaps modified) reminder phrase.

Following the corner of the eye, you'll next tap underneath the eye. This location is called the "bony orbit"—it's what keeps your eyes in your head! The point is above either cheekbone, below your eyelid. You should feel a section of your eye-socket there. Again, firm, two-fingered tapping on this point while repeating the reminder phrase.

Then you move on to the central part of your upper lip, directly below the nose. Use the same two-fingered tapping technique here, firm, and steady. When ready, repeat the reminder phrase again.

After the upper lip is the chin point. This point is actually slightly above your chin, but below your lower lip. There should be a slight crease in between those two areas. Tap in this crease using the same two-fingered method, repeating your reminder phrase.

Up next is the collarbone point. For those of you familiar with acupuncture, this is the point known as K27. Here, I actually prefer not to use the standard two-finger tapping technique. Instead, use your hand to make a fist. Tap the entire fist on the point where you'd locate the knot of a man's tie, right in between both collarbones. With this method you'll hit at least one, if not both, of your collarbone points. Once again, repeat the reminder phrase while you continue to tap.

The next point is a bit weird. Imagine if your body had a seam running up each side, as if you were sewn together. This point is located on that seam, approximately four inches underneath your armpit. Once you've located the point, tap on it using the standard two-finger method again and repeat your reminder phrase.

The final meridian point used in EFT is the top of the head. Rather than tapping on one point, you're actually going to tap in a circular pattern on top of the head. Make sure not to stray to the sides or back of the head, though! One last time, repeat your reminder phrase as you tap.

Congratulations, you've finished your first session!

Every time you finish a complete round of tapping on all nine points, I recommend pausing for a moment, remaining focused on the target, and taking a deep breath. Hold it in for a second or two before letting it out. This allows the effects of your Tapping session to sink in.

Now that you've completed one full session, you're ready to reevaluate.

## STEP FOUR AND A HALF: REPEAT

This isn't so much a new section as much as it's a recap of the steps that came before. Regardless, what follows in this "step" is vital to the process, as it involves recalibrating the target in preparation for an additional round of Tapping.

After you've finished taking a deep breath following the first session, it's time to remember your rating from step two. What rating did you settle on earlier? Remember how I said this number would be important later on when you tried to determine whether you had made progress or not? Here is where you assess whether you were successful or not.

Refocus on the target you chose back in step one—the same one you already rated. It's best if you do this re-rating process immediately after completing an EFT session since you'll already be focused on the target and the results will be fresh. I recommend concentrating on the target at all times until you've finished your daily EFT practice.

Now it's time to re-rate the target. You're simply taking the target and reapplying the same process learned in step two. Encapsulate your discomfort or distress surrounding the target on the zero-to-ten point scale, with zero representing the least distress and ten the most.

Do you have a new number? How does it relate to the rating you originally chose the first time around? Is your new rating higher? Lower? Equivalent?

As I said earlier, lower is better. You *want* the rating to go down after each session, because that signals you've made progress. Even a small change, say from six to five, indicates success. A large change is excellent and means you've landed on a particularly effective setup statement and are focusing on an excellent emotional target. Either way, you should be able to reuse the same setup statement for a repeat session, though perhaps with diminishing results.

If your second rating matched the first, you might need a better (more specific) setup statement. Remember, the setup statement is the most crucial aspect of EFT, and also the hardest to master. It's entirely possible the setup statement you chose earlier doesn't resonate enough emotionally, so you're not actually eliminating the problem through Tapping. I'd recommend revisiting your target and trying to come up with a more focused setup statement for the next session (for instance, "I need to stuff myself when I'm feeling anxious").

Finally, if your rating went *up* after the first round, there are two possibilities: either your earlier rating was artificially low because you weren't fully focused, or other deeply hidden emotions have come to the surface. I find both of these results are actually fairly common amongst my clients and very useful!

The first scenario suggests the EFT session you finished brought you more in touch with your emotions. You might have inadvertently rated your feelings about the target too low the first time around because you felt more detached. As you went through the first round of Tapping, you concentrated steadily on the target and brought it into focus. When you go to rate the same target the second time it will resonate even more.

This first situation actually occurs so often with my clients I often believe it's just a part of the process. Many people I've worked with need one good round of Tapping before they feel comfortable and come up with an open, honest rating. After that first session, the numbers start spiraling downwards.

The other scenario, wherein other angles arise during the course of the first session, actually isn't restricted to situations where the second rating is higher than the first, though I find the two often coincide. As you tap you become increasingly in-tune with the target. Eventually, you start to see past your initial setup statement and notice the subconscious, previously-hidden emotions at the root of the problem.

For instance, maybe you started out targeting overeating in general. You craft your setup statement around overeating, but you don't exactly know what emotion is at the root of the problem. As you go through your first round of Meridian Tapping, however, you start to reach deeper into the emotional cause. Eventually you realize your overeating stems from loneliness. Now you can go back to the beginning and start addressing your overeating habits as a symptom of underlying loneliness. This gives you a strong, resonant emotional core to build your EFT target and setup statement.

It's important not to get tunnel vision or zero in too closely on a single target. I want you to resolve every facet of the

problem, not just the surface-level issues. As you practice EFT, other angles will naturally present themselves to
you. Follow those angles! Go through the steps with those
angles! A number of times my clients have told me using
Tapping and focusing on positive energy lulled them into
a feeling of security, allowing these subconscious angles
to come out. They confess they probably never would
have thought of these hidden approaches without the help
of Meridian Tapping. It's important to make a note of
these hidden feelings while they're readily available so
you can address them later.

Only when you've addressed each angle will you notice
permanent progress in your overeating troubles. If you're
having trouble or feel stuck on any emotion, just switch
to a different one and continue the Tapping. Hopefully
by weakening the power of one angle you'll subsequently
weaken all angles.

Once you've re-rated, jump back into another Tapping
session and try to lower the discomfort caused by the target again.

The goal here is to get every target to as close to zero as
possible, by removing the "charge" on the problem. What
I mean is you want to strip the emotional charge from the
memory. You'll still remember the target, but the negative
energy and emotion will be gone. Once you've defeated
your own overeating habits, you'll wonder how those

emotions ever controlled your actions. Negative emotions are powerful and destructive, and it's a relief to eliminate their influence on your behavior.

I'm not saying it's easy, and certain stubborn traits or targets may require the help of a specialist, but you'll feel so much better afterward. Don't get discouraged if you're working on the same emotion across multiple sessions. Let it happen; take your time, and be thorough.

My aim with EFT is simple:

Release the conflict. Release the anxiety. Release the stress.

Let the chi flow freely through your meridians and expel all the toxic negative energies from your body.

Repeat steps two through four as many times as necessary until you've conquered your emotional overeating tendencies. EFT is a simple process to learn, but I've been working with the program for years and am still amazed sometimes at how powerful it is. It's an elegant, efficient process for people who need help making a positive change.

Anyone, even a complete newcomer to EFT, can use this book to overcome the indignities of emotional overeating. You now have the tool to combat your own bad habits.

Now it's simply a matter of knowing when to use this tool.

# CHAPTER FIVE

## The "When" of EFT

I said earlier that emotional overeating is one of the most problematic compulsive behaviors someone can experience. Food is everywhere! We all tend to stockpile food at home, even if we don't mean to, and going to the grocery store is a frequent activity. As if that weren't enough, food is required for survival. You can't just quit eating cold turkey. It doesn't work that way.

Alcoholics can avoid bars and other risky areas while recovering. Smokers can avoid cigarettes. But overeaters have to eat food to survive, so common triggers of cravings—the smell and sight of food—are prevalent.

Because food is everywhere, the hardest part of breaking an emotional overeating tendency is deciding when to use EFT. You already know how to *do* EFT. The steps in the last chapter provide you everything you need to know, and there are even more samples in the following chapter if you still need additional guidance.

But when do you use EFT in order to get the maximum effect?

I usually ask clients to go through a complete Tapping regimen two or three times a day, for at least five to ten minutes. Not a huge time commitment! When you're first starting out, those sessions might be a bit longer. Don't overwhelm yourself—a five to ten minute session will be more than enough to reset your energy system, reduce your stress, and maintain a positive outlook.

I recommend doing two of these EFT sessions at specific times of day: early in the morning immediately after waking, and late at night prior to going to sleep. The former prepares you to head off any cravings during the day, reducing your appetite at the start of the day and getting you in the right mindset. The session prior to sleeping helps you release the day's stress, and reduces the urge to use food to numb your feelings the following day.

The third session can occur anytime throughout the day. It's merely a reinforcement of the morning session, helping you reduce your stress, which is the culprit that fuels your appetite as you sit through the prime snacking hours in the afternoon. Of course, you're not *limited* to these three short sessions per day. If you're new to Tapping, you might pause and do a quick EFT session every hour or two just to refocus your brain and build up your determination. It's up to you, but the more Tapping sessions you do, the calmer you feel, the better you are able to handle cravings, worry, stress, and other challenging emotions that drive you to reach for food.

Any point where you start to notice your triggering emotions is an obvious time to do the third daily EFT session. For instance, maybe you've stuck with the program for a while and you know loneliness causes you to overeat. You're sitting at home after work and you start to feel lonely—the potential for binge eating is growing the longer you let that negative emotion fester.

Stop, breathe deeply, focus on the target emotion (loneliness, in this case), and begin a Tapping session to take the edge off the emotion. Allow hope and calm back into your life and head off any emotional overeating before it starts.

I don't recommend waiting until your cravings hit before you attempt to use EFT. Then the issue quickly becomes a battle of willpower. In the past, when my clients waited until a craving hit to use EFT it was a 50/50 chance whether or not they'd actually finish their sessions. It's not that I recommend refraining from tapping during those times. Quite the opposite, in fact. I strongly urge anyone experiencing an overwhelming craving to start tapping immediately. Just know there's a chance you might give in to the craving before you adequately combat the emotional root of the problem. That's why I recommend using Tapping on a regular basis, not just when a craving overcomes you.

It's much safer to head off those cravings before they hit by using Tapping at the onset of an emotional trigger or doing preventative maintenance sessions during the day. Remember, food is like a drug. It's much easier to say no to a drug *before* you have a craving. Once the craving gains traction, you may feel obsessed with satisfying it. You might slip back into your old patterns of behavior even though it's not your intention.

One great method I recommend to clients is to use Tapping before you open the refrigerator. Once the fridge is open, all bets are off! There's so much food calling out to you, begging to be eaten. If you can squeeze in a quick Tapping session *prior* to opening the fridge, however, you'll reduce the effects of any emotional triggers and make it easier to think objectively once the door is actually open.

In some cases you might even realize you were only looking for food out of boredom. EFT will reveal this emotional root, allowing you to leave the refrigerator door shut and go back to whatever you were doing. Eating because of boredom is an exceedingly common trait I see in my clients, and it's a dangerous habit to get into. Don't let apathy lead you into mindless eating.

Following from that, I also recommend using Tapping prior to any meals. While the "three square meals" idea is firmly entrenched in our culture, it's also a high-risk environment for overeating. Your body gets so hungry in between meals it's easy to overdo it by accident. You also bring any emotional baggage with you to the table, if you don't conduct an EFT session before eating. Strip away the negative emotional baggage, think rationally about your food, and take a portion that's, as Goldilocks would say, "Just right."

Even if you eat three meals a day, you might find there's another time where you tend to overeat. I've worked with many clients who stay up late, and unfailingly they complain about their nighttime snacking habits. If you know you're prone to eating unnecessary calories at a specific time of day, conduct an EFT session to head that off. Focus on your targets and clear them out so you can, again, get rid of the cravings before they grow any stronger and overwhelm your self-discipline.

The list goes on and on. I've had clients who've complained that the enticing smell of delicious food made them overeat, or seeing tasty food on advertisements led to overeating. I've had clients say sitting at a specific table causes them to overeat because it conjures up bad memories of their childhood. I've had clients say they associate food with calming themselves during a fight. Conversely, others say they associate food with love and safety.

Identify your triggers and work on eliminating them. You can't avoid food, but you can try to avoid or eliminate your *specific* triggers. Is that easy? Not necessarily, but it's a great start.

There's one last category of overeater I see relatively often, and that's people who don't feel safe losing weight. They want to try diets and programs, but in the end, taking the weight off feels "dangerous" to them. They anticipate feeling exposed or too vulnerable. If trepidation about losing weight is an issue for you – you feel "exposed" or too vulnerable without the protection of the extra weight– this is an excellent "tappable" issue, using the setup statement: "It's not safe for me to lose weight." If significant childhood trauma is the cause of you "needing" protection or feeling unsafe losing the weight, you also might need the support and guidance of a trained practitioner.

If that sounds like you, I strongly urge you to begin using Tapping whenever you feel those emotions surface. Feeling unsafe will cause you to sabotage your progress at every turn. It may take a while for you to make headway on your own, even if you practice every day, but I promise you *will* make headway. Consider consulting a trained practitioner if you feel stuck. Healing is possible with the right tools—you absolutely deserve a healthy, happy body and mind.

EFT can help get you there.

# CHAPTER SIX

## EFT Samples

I've given you all the steps you need to conduct your own successful EFT session, but I know the process can be a bit overwhelming when you're first starting out. I threw a lot of new concepts out at you in the past few chapters, and you may be wondering where to start when it comes to your own overeating tendencies.

In the interest of helping you out, I've compiled this chapter of sample exercises related to overeating and the feelings that trigger this behavior. These might not be the most personalized examples—in fact, they're pretty generalized—but they should give you a good foundation in some of the concepts I talked about earlier. Hopefully if you're ever feeling stuck in your own EFT sessions, or if you don't know where to start, this guide will serve as a handy reference.

There are all kinds of examples in the following pages. You'll find sample exercises for:

- Eating because of daily stress
- Eating to avoid emotions
- Eating because of loneliness
- Eating because you fear the future
- etc., etc.

All of the most common overeating triggers I've worked through with myself and my clients over the years are represented in this chapter. But you don't necessarily have to stick to my examples! Feel free to personalize your EFT program as you see fit. You'll get much better results when you're working with an emotionally resonant target, so I urge you to expand your horizons once you understand the basic framework covered in this chapter.

To start off, I think it would be helpful to list out the nine meridian points again, in order, without all of the exposition in between. If you ever get lost in the middle of an EFT session, you should be able to glance at this list and figure out which meridian point comes next, or consult the diagram in chapter four.

Below are the nine meridian points:

1) **Karate Chop Point** (Starts the session, along with the setup statement)

2) **Eyebrow**

3) **Side of the Eye**

4) **Under Eye**

5) **Under Nose**

6) **Chin**

7) **Collarbone** (K27 in acupuncture)

8) **Under Arm**

9) **Head**

I recommend running through these points as many times as necessary until you have them all memorized. With enough practice the order of the nine meridian points should become second nature, and that's a *good* thing. Having to guess at the next tapping point in the middle of a session just pulls your attention away from the target, diminishing your results.

If you run through one or more of the sample exercises below you'll get plenty of practice, so I'd recommend newcomers to EFT start there. The first example (overeating because of stress) has the most background information included, so read through that if you want to get a feel for the whole process again. The other examples are a bit more stripped down, with less background information. For that reason I recommend reading at least Clearing Example #1 and then skipping to whichever other examples interest you most.

# CLEARING EXAMPLE #1: OVEREATING BECAUSE OF DAILY STRESS

## STEP 1: Choose a Target

The target represents the emotion you're going to focus on in your Tapping session.

The target is the negative emotion, symptom, or event you choose to focus on during your EFT tapping session in order to modify your behavior. In this case, your habitual overeating stems from stress acquired throughout the day. It doesn't matter what the source of the stress is (though that might be a great angle to explore in later Tapping sessions). The stress simply causes you to eat in order to calm down. We want to break your stress-eating habit and replace it with a healthier, more positive behavior, so you choose a related target.

In this example, your target is:

*"I feel so stressed out."*

From this point on, everything in the example will relate back to this target.

## STEP 2: Rate the Intensity

Clear your mind and focus on the target: "I feel so stressed out." Before you can adequately rate your stress level, you need to fully embrace it. With a good target you'll *feel* the emotion right from the start.

We give a numerical rating to the target so you can measure your progress later on, after your EFT session has been completed. The scale measures emotional discomfort and distress. When you think of the target "I feel so stressed out," how distressed do you feel?

Attempt to rate your discomfort about the target on a zero-to-ten point scale, zero being the lowest possible amount of discomfort and ten being the highest.

I must remind you this rating is entirely subjective. Don't get too caught up in the numerical ratings. Go with your gut. Maybe a ten means every time you feel even a little stressed you resort to overeating to calm down, while a five means you only resort to overeating once in a while. It doesn't matter, as long as *you* know what your *personal* scale means. Nobody else will ever know these ratings, so it's up to you.

## STEP 3: Devise a Setup Statement

The setup statement is vital to the EFT process, but it's the part newcomers struggle with most. A good setup statement is incredibly easy to work with, providing excellent results with minimal effort. A poor setup statement, on the other hand, can feel like beating your head against a wall for all the good it does.

I'm fond of saying the setup statement is half the battle, and it's really true. A good setup statement will make the EFT process exponentially easier. A good setup statement encompasses what feels like the "truth" of the problem to you, combined with an acceptance phrase.

The setup statement in this example is highly generalized. You'll probably want to move on to something more personalized later on. This example is merely something I use to get my clients started, before we delve into their deeper emotions. Once you gain experience you'll have a better idea of how setup statements are constructed and how the overall EFT process works. At that point I recommend creating your own setup statement, perhaps by modifying this sample to fit your needs.

For the purposes of this example you'll use the following setup statement:

*"Even though I feel so stressed out that I can't stop eating, I deeply and completely accept myself anyway."*

Once you've read it over and have committed it to memory, it's time to begin the physical tapping process.

## STEP 4: Tapping

Each EFT session begins by tapping on the Karate Chop Point—the fleshy part on the outside of your hand (See diagram). As you do that, repeat the setup statement three times. Often, you don't repeat the exact same words each time, (although that is totally up to you). Instead, you say something that keeps the spirit of the setup statement while slightly changing the wording. This helps you to call up the "file" for the target you're modifying.

Begin by tapping on the **Karate Chop Point**. Then, while still tapping, focus on the target and say these statements:

First time: *"Even though I feel so stressed out that I can't stop eating, I deeply and completely accept myself anyway."*

Second: *"Even though I use food to make me feel calmer about my stress, I accept who I am."*

Third: *"Even though all this stress makes me overeat, I deeply and completely accept myself anyway."*

After the setup statement, you tap on the acupuncture points in sequence. At each point, you will also repeat the "reminder phrase." Like with the setup statement, you can be flexible and vary the wording of the reminder phrase each time you say it, helping your brain stay focused on the target rather than getting bored and saying the words without any emotional resonance.

Once you've said the third iteration of the setup statement, you're ready to begin tapping on the rest of the meridian points. You say the "reminder phrase" at each Tapping point as you proceed through the session. Each of these reminder phrases is a variation on the target, worded slightly differently to keep you focused and alert.

Then tap on the remaining meridian points, with the suggested reminder phrases:

**Eyebrow:** *"I'm overeating because I'm stressed out"*

**Side of the Eye:** *"I'm so stressed out."*

**Under Eye:** *"I feel so much stress in my life."*

**Under Nose:** *"I can't stop overeating."*

**Chin:** *"Food makes me feel better."*

**Collarbone:** *"I can't stop overeating when I feel stressed."*

**Under Arm:** *"The stress is really getting to me."*

**Head:** *"I feel so much stress."*

Once you've finished with the point on the top of your head, pause and take a deep breath and let it out slowly. Stay focused on the target. Let the effects of your EFT session sink in and relax. Now rate your stress level again, using the same system as step two. Did it change? Is it higher? Lower?

Ideally your level of discomfort has decreased. Eventually, you want your discomfort regarding the target to hit zero, though that might take several sessions to accomplish. With that in mind, do another round of Tapping with this same target and setup statement. Most targets will take multiple rounds to address completely.

Just like last time, begin by repeating the setup statement as you tap on the **Karate Chop Point**.

First time: *"Even though I have too much stress in my life, I choose to feel calm and peaceful."*

Second: *"Even though I have so much stress in my life that I keep overeating, I accept who I am anyway."*

Third: *"Even though I know I'm eating to relieve stress in my life, I choose to feel better about all of it."*

Next, tap on the meridian points and repeat your reminder phrases:

**Eyebrow:** *"I overeat because I'm stressed out."*

**Side of the Eye:** *"I feel way too much stress in my life."*

**Under Eye:** *"I feel way too much stress right now!"*

**Under Nose:** *"I can't stop overeating."*

**Chin:** *"I feel so stressed out."*

**Collarbone:** *"All this stress is making me want to overeat."*

**Under Arm:** *"I have all this stress bothering me."*

**Head:** *"I can't seem to calm down."*

Now, without stopping or losing focus on the target, let's do one last round of Tapping. You're going to skip the setup statements and start with the eyebrow point again. This time put a more positive spin on things. After reducing the strength of your discomfort, you're ready to hear some positive statements and options. After dispelling your negative emotions, you're now ready to do a few rounds of EFT focusing on positive suggestions.

**Eyebrow:** *"What if I could calm myself down without food?"*

**Side of the Eye:** *"I want to feel better and calmer."*

**Under Eye:** *"I wish I could feel calm and peaceful."*

**Under Nose:** *"What if I could feel better about the stress in my life?"*

**Chin:** *"What if I could calm myself down without food?"*

**Collarbone:** *"I choose to feel calm and peaceful."*

**Under Arm:** *"It feels so much better to feel calmer right now."*

**Head:** *"I love feeling calm and peaceful."*

When you've finished the third round, sit and breathe deeply. Rate your current stress level. Hopefully your rating has decreased yet again. Maybe it's even decreased quite a bit! Regardless, keep practicing, and feel free to adapt the setup statements and reminder phrases in this example to something more personalized when you're ready.

## CLEARING EXAMPLE #2: OVEREATING TO AVOID EMOTIONS

## STEP 1: Choose a Target

The target for EFT is the root emotional issue at the heart of your bad habits. I tell clients they can choose an event or symptom to target if necessary, but even these eventually boil down to an underlying emotion.

In later examples I'm going to explore a couple of particular negative emotions I commonly encounter in emotional overeaters, but this first example is very broad. I think this example could be particularly handy for people who don't know why they overeat yet, but who are willing to use EFT to find out. As you go through this example, you'll hopefully stumble upon the deeper emotions causing you to overeat.

This example could also be used by someone who overeats because of many simultaneous emotions, or someone who overeats because she or he doesn't want to feel *any* emotions.

In any case, the target here is:

*"I'm afraid to feel any strong emotions."*

## STEP 2: Rate the Intensity

Concentrate on your target, "I'm afraid to feel any strong emotions."

How does that statement make you feel? Do you feel uncomfortable because of that sentiment? Rate your fear on the zero-to-ten point intensity scale. Keep in mind that these ratings are entirely subjective and personal. Be honest with yourself.

Once you've noted down your rating, continue on to the setup statement.

## STEP 3: Devise a Setup Statement

In the past, clients I've met who eat to numb their emotions show some progress with the following setup statement:

*"Even though I'm afraid to feel my feelings so I overeat, I deeply and completely love and accept myself."*

Remember, this is an extremely generalized setup statement for an extremely broad target. As you become more comfortable with setup statements and the overall EFT process, I recommend diving in and personalizing your program.

When you've gotten a handle on the setup statement, you're ready to start tapping.

# STEP 4: Tapping

EFT sessions begin when you tap on the **Karate Chop Point** while repeating the setup statement three times. This process helps your brain focus on the target and understand which negative emotions you plan to release during the upcoming session.

For this example, begin tapping on the Karate Chop Point while repeating the following:

First time: *"Even though I use food to block my feelings because I'm afraid to feel them, I deeply and completely love and accept myself."*

Second: *"Even though I overeat so I don't have to feel my emotions, I accept who I am and how I feel."*

Third: *"Even though I overeat so I don't have to feel anything, I accept all of me anyway."*

At this point you're ready to begin tapping on the other eight points. At each point you'll say a variation of the "reminder phrase" to keep your brain focused on the task at hand.

**Eyebrow:** *"I don't want to feel my feelings."*

**Side of the Eye:** *"I'm afraid to feel my feelings."*

**Under Eye:** *"Overeating helps me avoid my strong emotions."*

**Under Nose:** *"I don't like these strong, upsetting emotions."*

**Chin:** *"No wonder I overeat."*

**Collarbone:** *"I don't want to feel all these feelings."*

**Under Arm:** *"I'm afraid to deal with these emotions."*

**Head:** *"Overeating helps me ignore these feelings."*

Now that you've finished this first session, pause and take a deep breath. Stay focused on the target—fear of feeling your emotions — and re-evaluate your emotional discomfort using the same process described in step two. How did your rating change? Remember, you eventually want all of your discomfort ratings to decrease to zero.

Keep repeating the process until you've brought your fear of feeling your emotions down to a manageable level and are feeling more calm and peaceful.

## CLEARING EXERCISE #3: OVEREATING BECAUSE OF LONELINESS

## STEP 1: Choose a Target

Loneliness is one of the most common emotions my clients anesthetize with overeating. Food becomes, in essence, their "friend." Rather than sitting around feeling lonely, they surround themselves with food to take the edge off.

If you're suffering from this problem, a great target to get started with is:

*"I overeat because I feel so lonely and empty."*

## STEP 2: Rate the Intensity

Focus on the target from step one, "I overeat because I feel so lonely and empty."

Devise an open and honest rating of your discomfort in relation to the target using the zero-to-ten point intensity scale. How lonely do you feel? How empty does your life feel? Remember, zero is the lowest amount of discomfort and ten the highest.

With that done, you're ready to proceed on to the setup statement.

## STEP 3: Devise a Setup Statement

If you eat to numb your feeling of loneliness, try experimenting with this setup statement:

*"Even though I feel lonely and that makes me want to overeat, I choose to accept myself anyway."*

This is a great starting point, though I advise you to create something more personal as you become more comfortable with the EFT process.

Say the setup statement a few times to get the wording down. Once you feel ready, proceed to the next step.

## STEP 4: Tapping

All EFT sessions start the same way. Begin tapping on the **Karate Chop Point** while saying three iterations of the setup statement or three variations on that theme.

In this example, repeat the following as you tap on the **Karate Chop Point**:

First time: *"Even though I feel lonely and that makes me want to overeat, I choose to accept myself anyway."*

Second: *"Even though I feel lonely and empty, I accept who I am and how I feel."*

Third: *"Even though I feel lonely and empty and I overeat, I accept who I am and how I feel."*

From here you'll begin tapping on the eight remaining meridian points, saying an accompanying "reminder phrase" at each one to keep your brain focused on the target.

**Eyebrow:** *"I feel so lonely and empty."*

**Side of the Eye:** *"I feel very alone and empty."*

**Under Eye:** *"I feel so alone."*

**Under Nose:** *"I feel lonely and just want to eat."*

**Chin:** *"I feel lonely and empty and it makes me want to eat."*

**Collarbone:** *"I feel empty and lonely and want to overeat."*

**Under Arm:** *"Overeating makes me feel better."*

**Head:** *"I feel lonely and empty."*

When you're done with the session, pause and breathe deeply. Concentrate on the target and measure how you feel on the zero-to-ten point scale. Note whether your new discomfort rating increased or decreased from the original.

Now you're going to repeat the Tapping process with more positive options. You could say the setup statements a second time, but it's not required. You're already focused on the target.

**Eyebrow:** *"It's hard not to overeat when I feel empty."*

**Side of the Eye:** *"I feel lonely and empty, but I don't have to overeat."*

**Under Eye:** *"I want to overeat when I feel lonely."*

**Under Nose:** *"What if I took care of myself instead?"*

**Chin:** *"What if I didn't need to use food to make myself feel better?"*

**Collarbone:** *"I don't need all this food."*

**Under Arm:** *"I want to feel better without all the extra food."*

**Head:** *"I choose to feel better even without the extra food."*

Again, pause and take a deep breath. When ready, re-evaluate the target and see where this new rating falls. Hopefully you've reduced your emotional discomfort closer to zero. Repeat the process as many times as possible, creating new and more personalized setup statements as you become more familiar with the process as a whole.

## CLEARING EXERCISE #4: OVEREATING BECAUSE OF ANGER

*Note: From here on out these examples will be extremely bare bones. I'm just going to provide you with the actual target, setup statement, and reminder phrases you'll need to proceed. If you need more background information, feel free to refer to one of the earlier exercises.*

## STEP 1: Choose a Target

If you find yourself overeating whenever you're angry, try out the following target:

*"I feel this underlying pent-up anger."*

## STEP 2: Rate the Intensity

Concentrate on the target, "I feel this underlying pent-up anger," and rate your discomfort using the zero-to-ten intensity scale.

## STEP 3: Devise a Setup Statement

If you overeat out of anger, this setup statement should help you get started:

*"Even though my pent-up anger makes me want to overeat, I deeply and completely love and accept myself anyway."*

Remember, it's always better to use a more personalized setup statement. Try to come up with your own once you feel more comfortable with EFT.

## STEP 4: Tapping

If you eat to quell your anger, repeat the following as you tap on the **Karate Chop Point**:

First time: *"Even though my anger makes me want to overeat, I deeply and completely love and accept myself anyway."*

Second: *"Even though I feel so angry, I accept myself anyway."*

Third: *"Even though I eat out of anger, I accept who I am and how I feel."*

Once ready, start tapping on the eight remaining meridian points while saying your reminder phrases.

**Eyebrow:** *"I have a lot of pent-up anger."*

**Side of the Eye:** *"I have so much pent-up anger."*

**Under Eye:** *"No wonder I overeat."*

**Under Nose:** *"I can't stop overeating."*

**Chin:** *"All this pent-up anger."*

**Collarbone:** *"So much anger from my life."*

**Under Arm:** *"It makes me want to overeat."*

**Head:** *"I don't want to feel it so I overeat."*

After you've finished tapping on the top of the head, pause and take a deep breath. Remain focused on the target and re-evaluate your discomfort level on the same zero-to-ten point scale. Repeat as necessary until your rating reaches zero, or lowers enough that you can continue on with your life in a healthy and positive manner.

## CLEARING EXERCISE #5: OVEREATING BECAUSE OF ANXIETY

### Step 1: Choose a Target

Let's choose the target "I feel so anxious." This is a common feeling for many people, not just overeaters. If you can tap down your anxiety, the desire to overeat will be significantly reduced.

### Step 2: Rate the Intensity

Measure how that feels to you on the zero-to-ten point scale.

### Step 3: Devise a Setup Statement

In this case, a good setup statement could be "Even though I feel so anxious I want to overeat, I deeply and completely love and accept myself anyway."

### Step 4: Tapping

We'll start as usual by tapping on the **Karate Chop Point**:

First: *"Even though I feel so anxious all the time, I deeply and completely love and accept myself anyway."*

Second: *"Even though I feel constant anxiety about my life, I accept who I am and how I feel."*

Third: *"Even though I feel this constant anxiety, and food relieves it temporarily, I accept who I am and how I feel."*

**Eyebrow**: *"I feel so anxious all the time."*

**Side of Eye**: *"I feel so anxious all day long."*

**Under Eye**: *"I don't know why I feel so anxious."*

**Under Nose**: *"I feel so anxious."*

**Chin**: *"This constant anxiety."*

**Collarbone**: *"Overeating calms me down."*

**Under Arm**: *"But I don't want to overeat anymore."*

**Head**: *"I'm not sure how to feel better."*

Now pause and take a deep breath. Rate your level of anxiety again, using the zero-to-ten point scale. When ready, let's run through a second session.

Let's go back and tap on the **Karate Chop Point** again, with a slightly revised setup statement:

First: *"Even though I suffer from constant anxiety, and it exhausts me, I deeply and completely love and accept myself."*

Second: *"Even though I still feel anxious and it makes me want to eat, I accept who I am and how I feel."*

Third: *"Even though I feel anxious all day long and I hate it, I deeply and completely love and accept myself anyway."*

**Eyebrow**: *"I still feel anxious."*

**Side of Eye**: *"I hate feeling so anxious all the time."*

**Under Eye**: *"I feel so anxious every day."*

**Nose**: *"I don't know how to calm down."*

**Chin**: *"I want to feel calmer."*

**Collarbone**: *"I choose to feel calm instead."*

**Head**: *"I appreciate the small moments of calm in my life."*

Now pause and take a deep breath. Rate your level of anxiety yet again, using the zero-to-ten point scale. Since you're already focused on the target, the next round will begin at the eyebrow.

Because anxiety is such a challenging emotion, and we all feel it at different times, I think it's a good idea to go through one more Tapping sequence, starting again at the eyebrow:

**Eyebrow**: *"Wouldn't it be nice to feel calm and peaceful?"*

**Side of Eye**: *"I choose to feel calm and peaceful."*

**Under Eye**: *"I love feeling just a little bit better."*

**Nose**: *"I appreciate feeling calm."*

**Chin**: *"I want to feel calm more often."*

**Collarbone**: *"I choose to feel calm and peaceful."*

**Head**: *"What a relief to feel calm and peaceful."*

Now repeat the target phrase again "I feel so anxious" and measure how that feels to you now on the zero-to-ten point scale. Keep using Tapping to quiet your anxiety, and I guarantee you will get relief. If you discover exactly what makes you feel anxious in your life, insert those words as your next target.

## CLEARING EXERCISE #6: OVEREATING BECAUSE OF INTENSE FOOD CRAVINGS

*Note: If you feel lost at any point during this exercise, jump back to one of the samples earlier in this chapter. In those examples I provided more background information for your benefit. The text below is simply an educational example of a successful EFT session.*

**STEP 1: Choose a Target**

This target is best used when you actually feel cravings. A great target for this particular exercise is:

*"I can't control my intense cravings."*

**STEP 2: Rate the Intensity**

Focus completely on the target, "I can't control my intense cravings." Rate your discomfort using the zero-to-ten point intensity scale. Note your rating—you'll be using it after your Tapping session is completed.

**STEP 3: Devise a Setup Statement**

I recommend this setup statement when you're dealing with food cravings:

*"Even though I have these intense cravings and can't control myself, I deeply and completely accept all of me anyway."*

While this is a great starting point, you'll get your best results from more personalized setup statements. Once you've run through a few EFT sessions, try creating your own. You'll be amazed what a difference it makes!

**STEP 4: Tapping**

While tapping on the **Karate Chop Point**, say the following setup statements to help your brain focus on the target:

First time: *"Even though I have these intense cravings and can't control myself, I deeply and completely accept all of me anyway."*

Second: *"Even though I can't control my cravings, I accept myself and how I feel."*

Third: *"Even though these intense cravings make me want to overeat, I deeply love and accept myself."*

At this point, it's time to tap on the other eight meridian points. At each point you'll say a reminder phrase to help keep your brain focused on the target and bolster your results.

**Eyebrow:** *"These intense cravings."*

**Side of the Eye:** *"All these intense cravings."*

**Under Eye:** *"I can't control myself."*

**Under Nose:** *"I don't want to control myself."*

**Chin:** *"I want what I want."*

**Collarbone:** *"Such intense cravings."*

**Under Arm:** *"I can't control my cravings."*

**Head:** *"I just want to eat something now."*

Now pause and take a deep breath. Rate your level of cravings a second time, using the zero-to-ten point scale.

When ready, start the second session. Since you're already focused on the target, this one will begin at the eyebrow.

**Eyebrow:** *"These intense cravings."*

**Side of the Eye:** *"I have so many feelings I want to eat over."*

**Under Eye:** *"I can't control myself or my cravings."*

**Under Nose:** *"They make me feel out of control."*

**Chin:** *"I want what I want and I want it right now."*

**Collarbone:** *"I can't stop thinking about eating."*

**Under Arm:** *"I can't control my cravings."*

**Head:** *"I just want to eat something now."*

When you've finished this second round, follow the same procedure: pause and take a deep breath. Then rate your feelings towards the target again. Hopefully you see an improvement! Otherwise, keep working at it. Repeat these steps as often as necessary until you've brought your discomfort down to a manageable amount—or zero!

## CLEARING EXERCISE #7: OVEREATING BECAUSE OF FEELING UNSAFE

*Note: If you get lost in this example, please refer to one of the earlier exercises where more background information is included.*

## STEP 1: Choose a Target

For this example, I recommend this as a starting target:

*"I overeat because I don't feel safe without weight as my protection."*

## STEP 2: Rate the Intensity

While focusing on the target, "I overeat because I don't feel safe without weight as my protection," use the zero-to-ten point intensity scale to rate your overall distress or discomfort.

## STEP 3: Devise a Setup Statement

If you overeat to sabotage your own weight loss, try starting with this setup statement:

*"Even though I don't feel safe without the extra weight, I deeply and completely love and accept myself anyway."*

Remember that, when possible, it's always best to use a personalized setup statement. Once you feel comfortable with EFT, I highly recommend devising your own instead of relying on this more generalized example.

## STEP 4: Tapping

Repeat these setup statements as you tap on the **Karate Chop Point**:

First time: *"Even though I'm afraid of reaching my goal weight because I'll feel unsafe and exposed, I deeply and completely love and accept myself anyway."*

Second: *"Even though I'm afraid I'll feel too vulnerable if I reach my weight loss goal, I accept who I am and how I feel."*

Third: *"Even though I hold all this fear of being exposed without the extra weight, I deeply and profoundly accept how I feel."*

From there you're ready to run through the remaining meridian points while saying the following reminder phrases to keep you focused on the target.

**Eyebrow:** *"I'm afraid to reach my goal weight."*

**Side of the Eye:** *"I won't feel safe without my protection."*

**Under Eye:** *"I'm afraid I'll feel exposed and unsafe."*

**Under Nose:** *"I'm afraid of feeling unsafe without the weight."*

**Chin:** *"I'm afraid I'll feel unsafe and exposed"*

**Collarbone:** *"I'm afraid of losing the weight."*

**Under Arm:** *"All this fear about losing the weight."*

**Head:** *"I'm afraid I won't feel safe without the extra protection."*

When you're finished, stay focused on the target as you pause and take a deep breath. Rate your discomfort level again by using the same zero-to-ten point scale from step two. Hopefully your rating decreased since the beginning of the session, demonstrating you've made progress. Regardless, repeat the Tapping as necessary until your rating has been sufficiently lowered.

# CONCLUSION

Congratulations! You've now taken your first steps towards addressing your emotional overeating habit. I just want to say I believe in you. I really think you can do it.

Why? Because I've seen this process work, on my clients and *myself*. I've beaten my own stress-fueled cravings using the same techniques outlined in this book. EFT is powerful, when you know how to use it.

Emotional overeating is, for many people, a fact of life, but it doesn't have to be. Your progress might not happen overnight. It might take you a few EFT sessions before you really start seeing a change in your emotions, your eating, and your weight. It might take many sessions before the problem is *completely* gone. But I promise, it *will* be gone if you work at it.

Even after you think it's gone for good, you might get hit with a sudden craving a few weeks from now. Don't worry! You can handle it. You now have the tools to completely defeat your habitual overeating, for now and in the future. It's going to take practice. It's going to take some effort on your part. Still, I know you're going to make it. You can persevere, and you can get through this.

If you ever need more support, feel free to stop by my website: www.attractingabundance.com. I have a lot of resources there to help people just like you conquer their emotions and find a happier, healthier lifestyle.

Before you go, I've got a little homework for you. Don't roll your eyes at me! It won't take long!

In fact, the homework is pretty consistent with what you've already been doing throughout this book. All I want you to do is **keep doing your Tapping.**

I recommend using Tapping every day, for at least 5-15 minutes. That's not too much of a time commitment in the grand scheme of things, but it will help keep your energy flowing and banish negative emotions from your mind and diminish the effects they have on your body. I call these sessions "maintenance," because you're merely ensuring your body stays on the right track for the future. Personally I recommend keeping your Tapping time in your calendar. This makes sure you'll stick to it *and* shows you're willing to focus on yourself when necessary. You're taking time for self-improvement, which is never a bad thing!

And once you've defeated your overeating habits, I want you to make Tapping a part of your life. EFT has so many other applications—you can use it to modify practically any negative behavior and feeling in your life. Experiment! The more you practice, the better you'll get at devising setup statements and clearing out stress and conflicts.

Emotional overeating doesn't have to control you. We've all done it, and we can all *stop doing* it—with the right tools. All we need is a little help from EFT.

# References:

1      Masheb,Robin M. and Carlos M. Grilo. "Emotional overeating and its associations with eating disorder psychopathology among overweight patients with binge eating disorder." *International Journal of Eating Disorders* vol. 39 (2006): 141-146.

2      Davis, Caroline, Shaelyn Strachan, and Marni Berkson. "Sensitivity to reward: implications for overeating and overweight." *Appetite* vol. 42 (2004): 131-138.

3      Heatherton, Todd F. and Roy Baumeister. "Binge eating as escape from self-awareness." *Psychological Bulletin* vol. 110 (1991): 86-108.

4      Van Strien, Tatjana and Machteld A. Ouwens. "Effects of distress, alexithymia, and impulsivity on eating." *Eating Behaviors* vol. 8 (2007): 251-257.

5      Meyer, Caroline and Glenn Waller. "The impact of emotion upon eating behavior: The role of subliminal visual processing of threat cues." *International Journal of Eating Disorders* vol. 25 (1999): 319-326.

6      Davis, Caroline and Jacqueline C. Carter. "Compulsive overeating as an addiction disorder: a review of theory and evidence." *Appetite* vol. 53 (2009): 1-8.

7        Slochower, Joyce. "Emotional labeling and over-eating in obese and normal weight individuals." *Psychosomatic Medicine* vol. 38 (1976): 131-139.

8        Brownell, K.D. and T.A. Wadden. "Etiology and treatment of obesity: understanding a serious, prevalent, and refractory disorder." *Journal of Consulting and Clinical Psychology* vol. 60 (1992): 505-517.

9        Visit Dr. Callahan's website, http://www.roger-callahan.com/, for more information.

10       You can find more regarding Gary Craig's EFT techniques at http://www.emofree.com.

Printed in Great Britain
by Amazon